sychiatric

Glossary

*The meaning of terms
frequently used
in psychiatry*

Third Edition

AMERICAN PSYCHIATRIC ASSOCIATION

Washington, D. C., 1969

AMERICAN PSYCHIATRIC ASSOCIATION

FOUNDED IN 1844

The Oldest National Medical Society in the United States

The objects of this Association are:

— To further the study of the nature, treatment, and prevention of mental disorders and to promote mental health;

— To promote the care of the mentally ill;

— To further the interests, the maintenance, and the advancement of standards of all hospitals for mental disorders, of outpatient services, and of all other agencies concerned with the medical, social, and legal aspects of these disorders;

— To make available psychiatric knowledge to other branches of medicine, to other sciences, and to the public.

published by   AMERICAN PSYCHIATRIC ASSOCIATION
PUBLICATIONS OFFICE
1700 Eighteenth Street, N.W.
Washington, D. C. 20009

Additional copies of this publication are obtainable from the publisher at $1.00 each. Quantity rates are available on request.

first edition   May 1957

second edition   April 1964

third edition   April 1969

published by   AMERICAN PSYCHIATRIC ASSOCIATION
1700 Eighteenth St., N.W.
Washington, D. C. 20009

PRESENTING THE THIRD EDITION

The American Psychiatric Association takes pride in presenting this Third Edition of *A Psychiatric Glossary,* which has proved so useful to hundreds of thousands of mental health workers and students over the past 12 years.

It is of interest that the first edition in 1957 contained somewhat fewer than 500 entries, nearly all of them derived from "dynamic psychiatry." At that time the new psychotropic drugs had just arrived on the scene, and their vast potential was not clearly perceived. The work of the Joint Commission on Mental Illness and Health was barely under way. The new approach to the nation's mental health problems, so eloquently articulated by the late John Fitzgerald Kennedy, was then but a dream in the minds of a few leaders.

By the time of the second edition in 1964, however, it was found necessary to add about 150 new terms derived primarily from psychopharmacology, neurophysiology, biochemistry, mental retardation, and community psychiatry.

Now, in the third edition, about 150 more terms have been added, many of them from community psychiatry and from related behavioral sciences. In addition, it has been necessary to reformulate many definitions to harmonize with the revised definitions and terms as they appear in the Second Edition of the official *Diagnostic and Statistical Manual of Mental Disorders* (American Psychiatric Association, 1968).

Thus successive editions of the Glossary reflect directions of growth and progress in the profession of psychiatry. May the Fourth Edition, perhaps five years hence, reflect similar progress!

The Association is grateful to the Task Force that prepared the Third Edition and to the members of the Committee on Public Information who were responsible for the earlier editions and contributed much to this one. We must also thank scores of members of the Association and friends in other disciplines who generously volunteered suggestions and advice.

LAWRENCE C. KOLB, M.D.
President
American Psychiatric Asociation

TO THE READER

The words that appear in *italics* in this glossary are also defined in it, making it convenient for the reader to cross-check one reference with another. Sometimes the abbreviation *q.v.* is used to encourage him to do so.

a

abreaction: Emotional release or discharge resulting from recalling to awareness a painful experience that has been forgotten (repressed) because it was consciously intolerable. The therapeutic effect sometimes occurs through discharge of the painful emotions, desensitization to them, and often, increased insight.

abstinence: Voluntarily denying oneself some kind of gratification; in the area of *drug dependence,* the state of being without the drug on which the subject is dependent. The "abstinence syndrome" is equivalent to *withdrawal symptoms,* and its appearance suggests the presence of physiological dependence or *addiction.*

accident prone: In psychiatry, special susceptibility to accidents due to psychological causes.

acrophobia: See *phobia.*

acting out: Expression of unconscious emotional conflicts or feelings of hostility or love in actions that the individual does not consciously know are related to such conflicts or feelings. May be harmful or, in controlled situations, therapeutic (e.g. in children's play therapy).

acute situational or stress reactions: See *gross stress reaction.*

adaptation: Fitting or conforming to the environment, typically by means of a combination of autoplastic maneuvers (which involve a change in the self) and alloplastic maneuvers (which involve alteration of the external environment). The end result of successful adaptation is termed *adjustment;* "maladjustment" refers to unsuccessful attempts at adaptation.

addiction: Dependence on a chemical substance to the extent that physiologic dependence is established. The latter manifests itself as withdrawal symptoms (the abstinence syndrome) when the drug is withdrawn. See also *drug dependence.*

adjustment: The relation between the person, his inner self, and his environment. See also *adaptation.*

Adler, Alfred: (1870-1937): Viennese psychiatrist. See *individual psychology, inferiority complex* (under *complex*), *compensation,* and *overcompensation.*

adrenergic: Activated or transmitted by adrenalin (e.g. *sympathetic nerve fibers*). See also *sympathetic nervous system.*

aerophagia: Excessive or morbid air swallowing.

affect: A person's emotional feeling tone. "Affect" and "emotion" are commonly used interchangeably.

affective disorder: Any *mental disorder* in which a disturbance of *affect* is predominant. This is a broad concept that includes *depressive neurosis* (see under *neurosis),* the *major affective disorders,* and *psychotic depressive reaction.*

affective personality: See *cyclothymic personality* under *personality disorders.*

aftercare: Continuing treatment and rehabilitation provided in the community to help the patient maintain and continue to improve his adjustment following a period of hospitalization.

aggression: In psychiatry, a forceful, physical, verbal, or symbolic attack. May be appropriate and self-protective, including healthful self-assertiveness, or inappropriate. Also may be directed outward toward the environment, as in *explosive personality,* or inward toward the self, as in *depression.*

agitated depression: A psychotic depression accompanied by constant restlessness. Sometimes seen in *involutional melancholia* (q.v.). See also *depression.*

agitation: Severe restlessness; a major psychomotor expression of emotional tension.

agnosia: The inability to recognize and interpret the significance of sensory impressions; usually due to an organic brain disorder.

agoraphobia: See *phobia.*

agraphia: See *speech disturbance.*

ailurophobia: See *phobia.*

akathisia: Originally, a difficulty in sitting down. More recently broadened to include restlessness and uncontrolled muscular movements; sometimes seen as side effects in the use of certain *psychotropic* drugs, such as the *phenothiazines.*

alcoholic paranoid state: An *alcoholic psychosis* that develops in chronic alcoholics, usually male, and is characterized by excessive jealousy and delusions of infidelity by the spouse.

alcoholic psychoses: A group of major mental disorders associated with organic brain damage and caused by poisoning from alcohol. Includes *delirium tremens, Korsakov's psychosis, alcohol paranoid state* (q.v.), and often *hallucinosis.*

Alcoholics Anonymous (AA): The name of a group composed of former alcoholics who collectively assist alcoholics through personal and group support.

alcoholism: Addiction to or psychological dependence on the use of alcohol to the point that it is damaging to one's physical or emotional health, interpersonal relations, or economic functioning. The inability of a person to do without drinking or to limit his drinking once he starts is presumptive evidence of alcohol addiction.

alexia (dyslexia): See *speech disturbance.*

algophobia: See *phobia.*

alienation: In psychiatry, the term is used variously. For example: In *depersonalization* phenomena, feelings of unreality or strangeness produce a sense of *alienation* from one's self or environment. In obsessional states (see *obsessions)* where there is fear of one's emotions, avoidance of situations that arouse emotions, and continuing effort to keep feelings out of awareness, there is *alienation* of affect. More broadly, the term is used to denote the state of estrangement the individual feels in cultural settings that he views as foreign, unpredictable, or unacceptable.

alienist: Obsolete legal term for a psychiatrist who testifies in court about a person's sanity or mental competence.

Alzheimer's disease: A pre-senile degenerative organic brain disease. The symptoms are similar to *Pick's disease* (q.v.).

ambivalence: The coexistence of two opposing drives, desires, feelings, or emotions toward the same person, object, or goal. These may be conscious or partly conscious; or one side of the feelings may be unconscious. Example: love and hate toward the same person.

ambulatory schizophrenia: An unofficial term for a person with schizophrenia who functions sufficiently well that he generally does not require hospitalization. If in a hospital, he is kept on open wards or he may be allowed the complete freedom of the community.

amentia: An old term meaning absence of intellect as in severe congenital *mental retardation* (q.v.). The basis of amentia is usually organic and due to a developmental lack of adequate brain tissue. To be distinguished from *dementia* (q.v.).

American Board of Psychiatry and Neurology (ABPN): A medical body of 12 members, four each appointed by the American Psychiatric Association, the American Neurological Association, and the American Medical Association, which examines and certifies candidates as specialists or diplomates in psychiatry, child psychiatry, neurology, and neurology with special competence in child neurology. ABPN was established in 1934.

American Psychiatric Association: The leading national professional organization in the United States for physicians who specialize in psychiatry. It also includes members from Canada, Central America, and the Caribbean Islands, and corresponding members from other countries. Founded in 1844 as the Association of Medical Superintendents of American Institutions for the Insane, the association changed its name to the American Medico-Psychological Association in 1891, and to its present name in 1921. In 1969 it had nearly 17,000 members.

amimia: See *speech disturbance*.

amines: Organic compounds containing the amino group ($-NH_2$). Of special importance in biochemistry and neurochemistry. See also *biogenic amines* and *catecholamines*.

amnesia: Pathological loss of memory; forgetting; a phenomenon in which an area of experience is forgotten and becomes inaccessible to conscious recall. It may be of organic, emotional, or mixed origin, and limited to a sharply circumscribed period of time.

    retrograde amnesia: Amnesia for events that occurred *before* a significant point in time.

    anterograde amnesia: Amnesia for events that occurred *after* a significant point in time.

amok: A term denoting a relatively rare syndrome seen primarily in Malayan men, in which the individual suddenly becomes frenzied, violent, and even homicidal. The "running amok" episode appears to be an acute dissociative state precipitated by some intense frustration.

amphetamines: A group of chemicals that stimulate the cerebral cortex of the brain. Often misused by adults and adolescents to control normal fatigue and to induce euphoria. Used clinically to treat *hyperkinesis* (q.v.) in some children and to control minor depressions and overeating in adults. Highly addicting.

anaclitic: Literally, leaning on. In psychoanalytic terminology, denotes dependence of the infant on the mother or mother substitute for his sense of well being (e.g. gratification through nursing). Normal in childhood; pathologic in later years if excessive.

anaclitic depression: An acute and striking impairment of an infant's physical, social, and intellectual development that sometimes occurs following a sudden separation from the mothering person. See also *depression*.

anal character: A personality type that manifests excessive orderliness, miserliness, and obstinacy. In psychoanalysis, a pattern of behavior in an adult that is believed to originate in the *anal stage* of infancy. See *psychosexual development*.

anal erotism: The pleasurable part of the experience of anal function. Anal erotism appears in disguised and sublimated forms in later life. See also *psychosexual development* and *anal character.*

anal phase: See *psychosexual development.*

analgesia: A state in which the sense of pain is lulled or stopped.

analysand: A patient in psychoanalytic treatment.

analysis: a common synonym for *psychoanalysis* (q.v.).

analytic psychology: The name given by the Swiss psychoanalyst, Carl Gustav Jung (1875-1961), to his theoretical system, which minimizes the influence of sexual factors in emotional disorders and stresses mystical religious influences. See also *Jung.*

anamnesis: The developmental history of an individual and of his illness, especially a patient's recollections.

anankastic personality: A synonym for *obsessive compulsive personality.* (See under *personality disorders*).

anesthesia: Absence of sensation; may result from nerve damage, anesthetic drugs, or psychological processes such as in *hysterical neurosis, conversion type* (see under *neurosis*) or *hypnosis.*

anhedonia: Chronic inability to experience pleasure. See also *hedonism.*

anima: In Jungian psychology, the inner being of an individual as opposed to the outer character or *persona* that he presents to the world. Further, the anima may be the more feminine "soul" or inner self of a man; the *animus* the more masculine soul of a woman. See also *Jung.*

anorexia nervosa: A syndrome marked by severe and prolonged inability to eat, with marked weight loss, amenorrhea (or impotence), and other symptoms resulting from emotional conflict. Most frequently encountered in young females.

Antabuse: Disulfiram, a drug used in *aversive treatment* (q.v.) of alcoholism. It blocks the normal metabolism of alcohol and produces increased blood concentrations of acetaldehydes, which cause very unpleasant reactions, including pounding of the heart, shortness of breath, nausea, and vomiting.

antidepressant: Drugs used in treating depressions.

antisocial personality: See under *personality disorder*.

anxiety: Apprehension, tension, or uneasiness that stems from the anticipation of danger, the source of which is largely unknown or unrecognized. Primarily of intrapsychic origin, in distinction to fear, which is the emotional response to a consciously recognized and usually external threat or danger. Anxiety and fear are accompanied by similar physiologic changes. May be regarded as pathologic when present to such extent as to interfere with effectiveness in living, achievement of desired goals or satisfactions, or reasonable emotional comfort. See also *panic*.

anxiety hysteria: An early psychoanalytic term for what is now called *phobic neurosis*. See under *neurosis*.

anxiety neurosis: See under *neurosis*.

aphasia: See *speech disturbance*.

aphonia: Inability to produce normal speech sounds. May be due to either organic or psychic causes.

apoplexy: See *stroke*.

apperception: Perception as modified and enhanced by the individual's own emotions, memories, and biases.

apraxia: See *speech disturbance*.

aptitude tests: Tests to measure an individual's various special skills and talents. Used in vocational counseling, such tests provide information regarding mechanical, clerical, musical, artistic, and other special aptitudes. By administering a range of multiple tests, it is also possible to measure such special skills as verbal reasoning, abstract reasoning, numerical ability, space relations, clerical speed and accuracy, mechanical reasoning, spelling, and grammar.

association: Relationship between ideas or emotions by contiguity, continuity, or by similarity. See also *free association*.

asthenic personality: See under *personality disorder*.

ataraxy: Absence of anxiety or confusion; calmness. Thus, *tranquilizers* are frequently called "ataractic" drugs.

atypical child: Nonspecific term for a child with distorted personality development. Applied most often to *autistic children* with perceptual handicaps and brain damage.

aura: In epilepsy, a premonitory, subjective sensation (e.g. a flash of light) that often warns the patient of an impending convulsion.

autism (autistic thinking): A form of thinking marked by extreme self-absorption and egocentricity, in which objective facts are obscured, distorted, or excluded in varying degrees.

autistic child: In child psychiatry, a child who responds chiefly to inner thoughts, who does not relate to his environment; his overall functioning is immature and he often appears retarded. It may be an extension of *early infantile autism,* a manifestation of brain damage, or a sign of *childhood schizophrenia.* See under *schizophrenia.*

early infantile autism (Kanner's syndrome): A syndrome beginning in infancy and characterized by self-absorption, inaccessibility, and inability to relate.

autoeroticism: Sensual self-gratification. Characteristic of, but not limited to, an early stage of emotional development. Includes satisfactions derived from genital play, masturbation, fantasy, and from oral, anal, and visual sources.

automatism: Automatic and apparently undirected behavior that is not consciously controlled.

autonomic nervous system: The part of the nervous system that innervates the cardiovascular, digestive, reproductive, and respiratory organs. It operates outside of consciousness and controls basic life-sustaining functions such as the heart rate, digestion, and breathing. It includes the *sympathetic nervous system* and the *parasympathetic nervous system.*

aversive therapy (conditioning): A treatment that suppresses undesirable behavior by associating a painful or unpleasant reaction with the behavior. Some examples are: the use of emetics or *Antabuse* (q.v.) with alcoholics, or the administration of an electric shock following the occurrence of some undesired behavior or symptom. Aversive therapy or conditioning is thought by some (but disputed by others) to be effective in the treatment of such disorders as *enuresis,* writer's cramp, *homosexuality, fetishism, transvestitism,* and *alcoholism.*

battered child syndrome: Physical injury to a child resulting from excessive beating, usually by a parent or parents and usually performed repeatedly over an extended period of time. The presence of mental illness in the parents may be presumed.

Beers, Clifford W. (1876-1943): Author of *A Mind That Found Itself* and founder, in 1909, of the National Committee for Mental Hygiene, now the *National Association for Mental Health.*

behavior disorders of childhood: a group of disorders occuring in childhood and adolescence that are less severe than psychoses but more resistant to treatment than *transient situational disturbances* (q.v.) because they are more stabilized and internalized. They are characterized by overactivity, inattentiveness, shyness, feelings of rejection, over-aggressiveness, timidity, and delinquency. The child who runs away from home or who persistently lies, steals, and teases other children in a hostile fashion falls into this category.

behavior therapy: Any treatment approach designed to modify the patient's behavior directly rather than inquiring into the dynamic causation. Typically, the psychopathology is conceptualized as maladaptive behavior. The treatment techniques are adapted from laboratory investigations of learning and may use principles of classical, instrumental, and traumatic avoidance *conditioning, reciprocal inhibition and desensitization,* simple extinction, etc.

behavioral science(s): While strictly speaking physiology, neurology, endocrinology, and other biologically-based sciences may be called behavioral sciences, the term is generally reserved for those sciences focussed on the study of man's interpersonal relationships, values, experiences, activities, and institutions, such as psychiatry, psychology, cultural anthropology, sociology, and political science.

behaviorism: A body of psychologic theory developed by *John B. Watson* (1878-1958), concerned chiefly with objectively observable, tangible, and measurable data, rather than with subjective phenomena such as ideas and emotions.

Bender-Gestalt test: A psychological test in which the subject is presented, one at a time, with nine distinctly different geometric designs and told to copy them on a sheet of paper. He may then be asked to redraw them from memory. As a test for visual-motor coordination and for immediate visual memory, it can be of great help in detecting brain damage.

bestiality: See *sexual deviation.*

biogenic amines: A group of *amines* (q.v.) formed in the living organism, some of which exert an important influence on nervous system activity. Includes *catecholamines* (q.v.) and *indoles* (q.v.).

birth trauma: Term used by Otto Rank (1884-1939) to relate his theories of anxiety and neurosis to the inevitable psychic shock of being born.

bisexuality: Presence of the qualities of both sexes in the same individual. In psychoanalytic theory considered to be a universal trait, so that each individual has both masculine and feminine traits and homosexual and heterosexual tendencies, latent if not overt.

Bleuler, Eugen (1857-1939): Eminent Swiss psychiatrist whose investigation of *dementia praecox* led him to the alternate term *schizophrenia,* now in common usage. His studies enriched the concept of this disorder.

blocking: A sudden obstruction and interruption in the train of thought or speech, typically in the midst of a sentence, due to unconscious factors. Although normal persons may occasionally experience blocking, it is commonly seen in a variety of mental disorders and most often in *schizophrenia.*

body image: The conscious and unconscious picture a person has of his own body at any moment. The conscious and unconscious images may differ from each other.

borderline state (borderline psychosis): An unofficial diagnostic term for a condition in which a person's symptoms are difficult to classify as either psychotic or nonpsychotic. The symptoms may shift quickly from one pattern to another, and often include *acting out* and behavior suggesting *schizophrenia.*

brain syndrome: See *organic brain syndrome.*

brain waves: See *EEG.*

Brigham, Amariah (1798-1849): One of the original thirteen founders of the American Psychiatric Association (1844) and the founder and first editor of its official journal, now the *American Journal of Psychiatry.*

bulimia: Morbidly increased hunger. Same as *polyphagia.*

CA: Abbreviation for chronologic (actual) age. See also *IQ*.

carbon dioxide therapy: See *shock therapy*.

carnal abuse: An unlawful mishandling of the genitalia of another human being. In some jurisdictions, anything from kissing to forcible rape is considered "carnal abuse".

castration: In psychiatry, usually the fantasied loss of the penis. Also used figuratively to denote state of impotence, powerlessness, helplessness, or defeat. See also *castration complex* under *complex*.

castration anxiety: Anxiety due to fantasied danger or injuries to the genitals. May be precipitated by everyday events which have symbolic significance and appear to be threatening such as loss of job, loss of a tooth, or an experience of ridicule or humiliation. See also *castration complex* under *complex*.

castration complex: See under *complex*.

catalepsy: A generalized condition of diminished responsiveness usually characterized by trance-like states. May occur in organic or psychological disorders or under hypnosis.

cataplexy: Momentary loss of skeletal muscular tone with resulting weakness.

catatonic state (catatonia): A state characterized by immobility with muscular rigidity or inflexibility and at times by excitability. Often a symptom of *schizophrenia*.

catchment area: In psychiatry, a term borrowed from the English to delineate geographic area for which a mental health facility has responsibility. See also *community psychiatry*.

catecholamines: A group of *biogenic amines* derived from phenylalanine and containing the catechol nucleus. Certain of these amines, such as *epinephrine* and *norepinephrine,* exert an important influence on nervous system activity.

catharsis: (1) The healthful (therapeutic) release of ideas through a "talking out" of conscious material accompanied by the appropriate emotional reaction. (2) The release into awareness of repressed (i.e. "forgotten") material from the unconscious.

cathexis: Attachment, conscious or unconscious, of emotional feeling and significance to an idea or object, most commonly a person.

causalgia: A sensation of burning pain of either organic or psychic origin.

central nervous system (CNS): The brain and spinal cord.

central (syntactical) aphasia: See *speech disturbance.*

cephalalgia: Headache or head pain.

cerea flexibilitas: The "waxy flexibility" often present in catatonic schizophrenia in which the patient's arm or leg remains passively in the position in which it is placed.

cerebral arteriosclerosis: Hardening of the arteries of the brain resulting in an *organic brain syndrome* that may be either primarily neurologic in nature (e.g. convulsions, *aphasia,* chorea, athetosis, *parkinsonism,* etc.), or primarily mental (e.g. intellectual dulling, memory defects, emotional *lability,* paranoid delusions, confusion, and finally profound dementia), or a combination of both. Cerebral arteriosclerosis typically manifests itself in people over 50 years of age and at the present time accounts for approximately one-fifth of all first admissions to mental hospitals.

character: In psychiatry, the sum of the relatively fixed personality traits and habitual modes of response of an individual.

character analysis: Psychoanalytic treatment aimed at the *character defenses.*

character defense: In psychiatry, any character or personality trait which serves an unconscious defensive purpose. See also *defense mechanism.*

character disorder: A personality disorder manifested by a chronic and habitual pattern of reaction that is maladaptive in that it is relatively inflexible, limits the optimal use of potentialities, and often provokes the very counterreactions from the environment that the subject seeks to avoid. In contrast to symptoms of neurosis, character traits are typically *egosyntonic.* See also *personality.*

character neurosis: Similar to *character disorder* except that the neurotic conflicts are expressed in exaggerated but socially acceptable patterns of behavior and may not be easily recognizable as symptoms.

child analysis: Application of modified psychoanalytic methods and goals to problems of children to remove impediments to normal personality development.

childhood schizophrenia: See under *schizophrenia.*

cholinergic: Activated or transmitted by acetylcholine (e.g. *parasympathetic nerve fibers).* See also *parasympathetic nervous system.*

chromosomes: Microscopic intracellular structures that carry the *genes* for that cell. The normal human cell contains 46 chromosomes.

claustrophobia: See *phobia.*

climacteric: Menopausal period in women. Also used sometimes to refer to the corresponding age period in men.

clinical psychologist: See *psychologist, clinical.*

cognitive: refers to the mental process of comprehension, judgment, memory, and reasoning, as opposed to emotional and volitional processes.

collective unconscious: In Jungian theory, a portion of the unconscious common to all mankind; also called "racial unconscious." See *unconscious* and *Jung.*

combat fatigue: Term for disabling physical and emotional reaction incident to military combat. Paradoxically, the reaction may not necessarily include fatigue.

commitment: In psychiatry, a legal process for admitting a mentally ill person to a mental hospital, usually without his consent. The legal definition and procedure vary from state to state. Typically requires a court or judicial procedure, although not in all states, and sometimes the commitment may be entirely voluntary. A "voluntary" commitment, however, is to be distinguished from a "voluntary admission" in that in the former case the hospital has the right to detain the patient for a legally defined period of time after he has given notice that he wishes to leave. See also *habeas corpus.*

communication, privileged: See under *privilege.*

community mental health center: In general, a community or neighborhood-based facility, or a network of component facilities, for the prevention and treatment of mental illness, ideally with emphasis on a comprehensive range of services and with convenient accessibility to the population it serves. Since 1964, regulations governing federal support for community centers have required that a center offer at least five services, namely, inpatient, outpatient, partial hospitalization, emergency services, and consultation and education for community agencies. It is also considered desirable that a center should provide diagnostic, rehabilitative, precare and aftercare services, training, research, and public education.

community psychiatry: That branch of psychiatry concerned with the provision and delivery of a coordinated program of mental health care to a specified population (usually all residents of a designated geographical area termed the *catchment area*). Implicit in the concept of community psychiatry is acceptance of continuing responsibility for all the mental health needs of the community — diagnosis, treatment. rehabilitation (tertiary *prevention*) and aftercare, and, equally important, early case-finding (secondary *prevention*), and promoting mental health and preventing psychosocial disorder (primary *prevention*). The organizational nucleus for such services is typically the *community mental health center.* The body of knowledge and theory on which the methods and techniques of community psychiatry are based is often called *social psychiatry* (q.v.). See also *preventive psychiatry.*

compensation: (1) A *defense mechanism,* operating unconsciously, by which the individual attempts to make up for (i.e. to compensate for) real or fancied deficiencies. (2) A conscious process in which the individual strives to make up for real or imagined defects of physique, performance, skills, or psychological attributes. The two types frequently merge.

compensation neurosis: An unofficial term for certain unconscious neurotic reactions in which features of *secondary gain* (q.v.), such as a situational or financial advantage, are prominent. To be distinguished from *malingering* (q.v.) where there is conscious concealment or an ulterior motive to defraud. See also *hysterical neurosis, conversion type,* under *neurosis.*

complex: A group of associated ideas that have a common strong emotional tone. These are largely unconscious and significantly influence attitudes and associations. Three examples are:

castration complex: A group of emotionally charged ideas that are unconscious and which refer to the fear of losing the genital organs, usually as punishment for forbidden sexual desires; includes the childhood fantasy that female genitals result from loss of a penis.

inferiority complex: (Adler) Feelings of inferiority stemming from real or imagined physical or social inadequacies that may cause anxiety or other adverse reactions. The individual may overcompensate by excessive ambition or by the development of special skills, often in the very field in which he was originally handicapped. See also *overcompensation.*

Oedipus complex: (Freud) Attachment of the child for the parent of the opposite sex, accompanied by envious and aggressive feelings toward the parent of the same sex. These feelings are largely repressed (i.e., made unconscious) because of the fear of displeasure or punishment by the parent of the same sex. In its original use, the term applied only to the male.

compression: In psychiatry and neurology, the squeezing of the brain, spinal cord, or nerve fibers by such conditions as fractures, blood clots, tumors, and abscesses.

compulsion: An insistent, repetitive, intrusive, and unwanted urge to perform an act that is contrary to the person's ordinary wishes or standards. Since it serves as a defensive substitute for still more unacceptable unconscious ideas and wishes, failure to perform the compulsive act leads to overt anxiety. Compulsions are *obsessions* (q.v.) that are still felt as *impulses* (q.v.).

compulsive personality: A personality characterized by excessive adherence to rigid standards. Typically, the individual is inflexible, overconscientious, overinhibited, unable to relax, and exhibits repetitive patterns of behavior. See *obsessive compulsive personality* under *personality disorder*.

conative: Pertains to the basic strivings of an individual, as expressed in his behavior and actions; volitional as opposed to *cognitive*.

concussion: The impairment of brain function due to injury caused by a blow on the head. The speed and degree of recovery depend on severity of the brain injury. Symptoms include unconsciousness, disorientation, and paralysis.

condensation: A psychologic process often present in dreams in which two or more concepts are fused so that a single symbol represents the multiple components.

conditioning: Any process by which an individual learns — either consciously or unconsciously — to modify his behavior in the presence of a particular stimulus. Conditioning is employed clinically in *behavior therapy*.

classical (Pavlovian) conditioning: A *conditioning* process by which an individual learns to make a response mediated primarily by the *autonomic nervous system* (e.g. salivation or pupillary constriction) in the presence of a stimulus that normally does not elicit that response (i.e., a "neutral conditioned stimulus"). This is done by repeatedly exposing the individual to the neutral conditioned stimulus (e.g. the sound of a bell) at the same time or soon before he is exposed to the "unconditioned stimulus" (e.g. food or a bright light) that normally elicits that response in an untrained individual. When it occurs regularly in the presence of the neutral conditioned stimulus, the response is called a "conditioned reflex."

instrumental (operant) conditioning: A *conditioning* process by which an individual learns to make (or to avoid making) specific responses in the presence of a once-neutral stimulus. Conditioning is achieved by repeatedly presenting the individual with a rewarding (or punishing) stimulus after he has performed (or avoided performing) the particular response. The once-neutral stimulus is called a "conditioned stimulus"; and the rewarding (or punishing) stimulus is called a "reinforcing" or "unconditioned" stimulus.

traumatic avoidance: A form of instrumental conditioning in which, after a signal, a particular response must be completed in order to avoid a highly aversive stimulus. Once learned, this type of response is extremely resistant to extinction, particularly when it is difficult for the individual to find out that the traumatic consequences no longer obtain.

confabulation: The more or less unconscious, defensive "filling in" of actual memory gaps by imaginary experiences, often complex, that are recounted in a detailed and plausible way. Seen principally in organic psychotic disorders, such as *Korsakov's psychosis.*

confidentiality: In medicine, the ethical principle that a physician may not reveal the confidences entrusted or any information gained by him in the course of medical attendance, unless he is required to do so by law or unless it becomes necessary in order to protect the welfare of the individual or of the community. See also *privilege, privileged communication.*

conflict: In psychiatry, a mental struggle that arises from the simultaneous operation of opposing impulses, drives, or external (environmental) or internal demands; termed *intrapsychic* when the conflict is between forces within the personality, *extrapsychic* when it is between the self and the environment.

confusion: In psychiatry, refers to disturbed orientation in respect to time, place, or person.

congenital: Literally, present at birth. Not synonymous with hereditary or genetic, for it may include conditions that arise during fetal development or the birth process. It does not refer to conditions that appear after birth.

conscience: The morally self-critical part of the self-encompassing standards of behavior, performance, and value judgments. Commonly equated with the conscious *superego.*

constitution: A person's intrinsic physical and psychological endowment; sometimes used more narrowly to indicate the physical inheritance or potential from birth.

constitutional types: Constellations of morphologic, physiologic, and psychologic traits as earlier proposed by various scholars. Galen, Kretschmer, and Sheldon proposed the following major types: *Galen*: sanguine, melancholic, choleric, and phlegmatic types; *Kretschmer*: pyknic (stocky), asthenic (slender), athletic, and dysplastic (disproportioned) types; *Sheldon*: ectomorphic (thin), mesomorphic (muscular), and endormorphic (fat) types, based on the relative preponderance of outer, middle, or inner layers of embryonic cellular tissue.

contusion: A superficial injury produced by a nonlacerating impact; a bruise.

conversion: A *defense mechanism,* operating unconsciously, by which intrapsychic conflicts that would otherwise give rise to anxiety are, instead, given symbolic external expression. The repressed ideas or impulses, plus the psychologic defenses against them, are converted into a variety of somatic symptoms. Example: psychogenic paralysis of a limb that prevents its use for aggressive purposes.

conversion neurosis (reaction): See *hysterical neurosis, conversion type,* under *neurosis.*

convulsive disorders: Primarily the centrencephalic seizures, grand mal and petit mal, and the focal seizures of Jacksonian and psychomotor *epilepsy* (q.v.) These brain disorders, with their fairly characteristic electroencephalographic patterns, are to be differentiated from a variety of other pathophysiological conditions in which a convulsive seizure may occur. For example, seizures may follow withdrawal from alcohol, barbiturates, and a wide variety of other drugs; they may also occur in cerebral vascular disease, brain tumor, brain abscess, hypoglycemia, hyponatremia, high fevers, eclampsia, uremia, and many other metabolic and intracranial disorders. Finally, hysterical seizures and seizures simulated by *malingerers* may, at times, pose difficult diagnostic problems.

coping mechanisms: Ways of adjusting to environmental stress without altering one's goals or purposes; includes both conscious and unconscious mechanisms.

coprophagia: Eating of filth or feces.

coprophilia: Excessive or morbid interest in filth or feces or symbolic representations thereof.

counterphobia: The desire or seeking out of experiences that are consciously or unconsciously feared.

countertransference: The psychiatrist's conscious or unconscious emotional reaction to his patient. See also *transference.*

cretinism: A type of mental retardation and body malformation caused by severe uncorrected thyroid deficiency in infancy and early childhood.

criminally insane: A legal term for psychotic patients who have been found not guilty of a serious crime, such as murder, rape, or arson, "by reason of insanity." See also *Currens Formula, Durham, McNaghten Rule.*

crisis intervention: A type of brief treatment in which a therapist or team of therapists assist a patient and his family with an immediate problem by giving medication, altering environmental circumstances, suggesting changes in patterns of behavior, and making referrals to community agencies.

cross-cultural psychiatry: The comparative study of mental illness and mental health among different societies, nations, and cultures. The latter term is often used synonomously with *transcultural psychiatry,* the "trans" prefix denoting that the vista of the scientific observer extends beyond the scope of a single cultural unit.

cultural anthropology: The study of man and his works, or of the learned behavior of man: his technology, languages, religions, values, customs, mores, beliefs, social relationships, and family life and structure. Originally restricting its studies to primitive or pre-literate societies and to nonoccidental civilized societies, cultural anthropology in recent years has enlarged its scope of interest to include studies of contemporary Western cultures. Of particular interest to psychiatry is the finding that what is considered as psychopathological is a matter of consensus within a given society. Similar to *social anthropology* and *ethnology*.

cultural psychiatry: A branch of *social psychiatry* (q.v.) that concerns itself with the mentally ill in relation to their cultural environment. Symptoms of behavior regarded as quite evident psychopathology in one society may well be regarded as acceptable and normal in another society.

cunnilingus: Sexual activity in which the mouth and tongue are used to stimulate the female genitals.

Currens Formula: A ruling that a person is not responsible for a crime if, as a consequence of a mental disorder, he did not have "adequate capacity to conform his conduct to the requirements of the law." This formula is applied only in the federal (not the state) courts of Pennsylvania, Delaware and New Jersey, the Third U.S. Circuit. See also *McNaghten Rule* and *Durham*.

cybernetics: Term introduced by Norbert Wiener (1894-1964) to designate the science of control mechanisms. It covers the entire field of communication and control in machines and puts forth the hypothesis that there is some similarity between the human nervous system and electronic control devices.

cyclothymic personality: See under *personality disorder*.

day hospital: See under *partial hospitalization*.

death instinct (Thanatos): In Freudian theory, the unconscious drive toward dissolution and death. Co-exists with and is in opposition to the life instinct (Eros).

defense mechanism: Unconscious intrapsychic processes that are employed to seek relief from emotional conflict and freedom from anxiety. Conscious efforts are frequently made for the same reasons, but true defense mechanisms are out of awareness (unconscious). Some of the common defense mchanisms defined in this glossary are: *compensation, conversion, denial, displacement, dissociation, idealization, identification, incorporation, introjection, projection, rationalization, reaction formation, regression, repression, sublimation, substitution, symbolization, undoing.* See also *mental mechanism.*

déjà vu: The sensation that what one is seeing has been seen before.

delirium: A mental state characterized by confusion and altered, possibly fluctuating, consciousness. Delusions, illusions, hallucinations, and lability of emotions, particularly anxiety and fear, are often present.

delirium tremens: An acute and sometimes fatal disorder involving impairment of brain tissue; usually caused by withdrawal from excessive and unusually prolonged alcohol intake and manifested by tremors, frightening *illusions, hallucinations,* and sometimes convulsions. See also *organic brain syndrome.*

delusion: A false belief out of keeping with the individual's level of knowledge and his cultural group. The belief results from unconscious needs and is maintained against logical argument and despite objective contradictory evidence. Common delusions include:

delusions of grandeur: Exaggerated ideas of one's importance or identity.

delusions of persecution: Ideas that one has been singled out for persecution. See also *paranoia.*

delusions of reference: Incorrect assumption that certain casual or unrelated events or the behavior of others apply to oneself. See also *paranoia.*

dementia: An old term denoting madness or insanity; now used to denote organic loss of intellectual function.

dementia praecox: Obsolescent descriptive term for *schizophrenia*. Introduced by Morel (1860) and later popularized by *Kraepelin*.

dementia, senile: See *senile dementia*.

demography: The description of populations in terms of relevant variables such as size, density, growth trends, sex, and age distribution. Such data are frequently related to the incidence and prevalence of disease in the companion science, *epidemiology*.

denial: A defense mechanism, operating unconsciously, used to resolve emotional conflict and allay anxiety by disavowing thoughts, feelings, wishes, needs, or external reality factors that are consciously intolerable.

dependency needs: Vital needs for mothering, love, affection, shelter, protection, security, food, and warmth. May be a manifestation of regression when they reappear openly in adults.

depersonalization: Feelings of unreality or strangeness concerning either the environment or the self or both. See also *neurosis*.

depersonalization neurosis: See under *neurosis*.

depression: Psychiatrically, a morbid sadness, dejection, or melancholy. To be differentiated from grief, which is realistic and proportionate to what has been lost. A depression may be a symptom of any psychiatric disorder or may constitute its principal manifestation. Neurotic depressions are differentiated from psychotic depressions in that they do not involve loss of capacity for reality testing. The major psychotic depressions include *psychotic depressive reaction* and the various *major affective disorders.* (q.v.)

depressive neurosis: See under *neurosis*.

depressive psychosis: See *psychotic depressive reaction*.

deprivation, emotional: A lack of adequate and appropriate interpersonal and/or environmental experience, usually in the early developmental years.

deprivation, sensory: See *sensory deprivation*.

depth psychology: The psychology of unconscious mental processes. Also a system of psychology in which the study of such processes plays a major role, as in *psychoanalysis.*

dereistic: Describes mental activity that is not in accordance with reality, logic, or experience. Similar to autistic. See *autism.*

descriptive psychiatry: A system of psychiatry based upon observation and study of readily observable external factors; to be differentiated from *dynamic psychiatry.* Often used to refer to the systematized descriptions of mental illnesses formulated by *Kraepelin.*

desoxyribonucleic acids: See *DNA.*

deterioration: Worsening of a clinical condition, usually expressed as progressive impairment of function; in organic brain syndromes, for example, deterioration refers to a progressive loss of intellectual faculties without implying permanency of change. *Dementia,* in contrast, usually refers to an irreversible decline of mental functions with intellectual disintegration of such a degree as to render fragmentary or to falsify entirely the patient's relationship to his environment. *Regression,* on the other hand, implies that the decline in functioning is reversible, and is more often applied to impairment in the emotional sphere than to intellectual impairment.

determinism: In psychiatry, the postulate that nothing in the individual's emotional or mental life results from chance alone but rather from specific causes or forces known or unknown.

dipsomania: See *–mania.*

Diagnostic and Statistical Manual of Mental Disorders: A manual that lists and defines all of the psychiatric diagnoses recognized by the American Psychiatric Association as acceptable for use in the United States. The first edition (DSM-I) was published in 1952, and the second (DSM-II) in 1968. See also *International Classification of Diseases.*

disorientation: Loss of awareness of the position of the self in relation to space, time, or other persons; confusion.

displacement: A *defense mechanism,* operating unconsciously, in which an emotion is transferred or "displaced" from its original object to a more acceptable substitute.

dissociation: A *defense mechanism,* operating unconsciously, through which emotional significance and affect are separated and detached from an idea, situation, or object. Dissociation may defer or postpone experiencing some emotional impact as, for example, in selective *amnesia.*

dissociative reaction: Same as *hysterical neurosis, dissociative type* (q.v. under *neurosis*).

distributive analysis and synthesis: The therapy used by the psychobiologic school of psychiatry developed by *Adolf Meyer.* Entails extensive guided and directed investigation and analysis of the patient's entire past experience, stressing his assets and liabilities to make possible a constructive synthesis. See *psychobiology.*

Dix, Dorothea Lynde (1802-1887): Foremost nineteenth century American crusader to improve institutional care of the mentally ill.

DNA (desoxyribonucleic acid): One of the key chemicals governing life functions. Found in the cell nucleus. Essential constituent of the *genes.* Governs the manufacture of *RNA.*

dominance: 1) In psychiatry, an individual's disposition to play a prominent or controlling role in his interaction with others. 2) In neurology, the (normal) tendency of one half of the brain to be more important than the other in controlling behavior (cerebral dominance). 3) In genetics, the ability of one *gene* (dominant gene) to express itself in the *phenotype* of an individual, even though that gene is paired with another (recessive gene) that would have expressed itself in a different way.

double bind: A type of interaction, noted frequently in families with schizophrenic members, in which one person (often the mother) demands a response to a message containing mutually contradictory signals while the other (the schizophrenic son, for example) is unable either to comment on the incongruity or to escape from the situation. Example: a mother tells her son to act like a man and express his opinion and when he does, berates him as unloving and disloyal.

double-blind study: A research procedure for testing the therapeutic effectiveness of a drug. Neither the research investigator nor the patients know whether the drug being given is the one under investigation, another drug, or a *placebo* until the completion of the study.

double personality: See *personality, multiple.*

Down's syndrome (disease): Preferred term for a common form of mental retardation caused by a chromosomal abnormality; formerly called *mongolism,* a name increasingly regarded as inappropriate and inaccurate.

drawing test: A psychological test in which the subject is asked to draw (but not copy) a person, and then another person of the opposite sex, a tree, a house, an animal, or any other object. Attitudes and traits that are important to the subject may be revealed by the type of body posture he depicts, movements, size of person, omission or distortion of body parts, sex differentiation, etc. Although not as informative as the *Thematic Apperception Test (TAT)* and the *Rorschach Test,* the drawing tests offer rather quick and helpful information about problems that may not be very deep-seated but that are troublesome to the subject.

drive: Basic urge, instinct, motivation; in psychiatry, a term currently preferred to avoid confusion with the more purely biological concept of *instinct.*

drug abuse: See under *drug dependence.*

drug dependence: Habituation to, abuse of, and/or addiction to a chemical substance. Largely because of psychologic craving, the life of the drug-dependent person revolves about his need for the specific effect of one or more chemical agents on his mood or state of consciousness. The term thus includes not only *addiction,* (which emphasizes physiologic dependence), but also drug abuse, (where the pathologic craving for drugs seems unrelated to physical dependence). *Alcoholism* is a special type of drug dependence. Other examples are dependence on opiates; synthetic analgesics with morphine-like effects; barbiturates; other hypnotics, sedatives, and tranquilizers; cocaine; marihuana; other psychostimulants; and hallucinogens.

DSM-II: Abbreviation for *Diagnostic and Statistical Manual of Mental Disorders,* Second Edition (q.v.).

dummy: British term for *placebo.*

Durham Decision: A ruling which states that a person is not responsible for a crime if his act was the product of mental disease or defect. Currently, this formula applies only in the District of Columbia and the State of Maine. See also *McNaghten Rule* and *Currens Formula.*

dyadic: The relationship between a pair. In psychiatry, refers to the therapeutic relationship between doctor and patient as in "dyadic therapy."

dynamic psychiatry: As distinguished from *descriptive psychiatry* (q.v.), refers to the study of emotional processes, their origins, and the mental mechanisms. Implies the study of the active, energy-laden, and changing factors in human behavior and its motivation. Dynamic principles convey the concepts of change, of evolution, and of progression or regression.

dynamics: See *psychodynamics.*

dysarthria: Impaired, difficult speech, usually due to organic disorders of the nervous system or speech organs.

dyslexia: See *speech disturbance.*

dyspareunia: Pelvic pain, usually emotional in origin, experienced by the female in sexual intercourse.

dysphagia: Difficult or painful swallowing.

dyssocial behavior: In psychiatry, a diagnostic term for individuals who are not classifiable as *anti-social personalities,* but who are predatory and follow more or less criminal pursuits such as racketeers, dishonest gamblers, prostitutes, and dope peddlers. Formerly called "sociopathic personalities."

early infantile autism: See under *autism*.

echolalia: The pathologic repetition by imitation of the speech of another. Sometimes seen in *schizophrenia, catatonic type*.

echopraxia: The pathologic repetition, by imitation, of the movements of another. Sometimes seen in *schizophrenia, catatonic type*.

ecology: Study of relations between individuals and their environments. In psychiatry, especially the study of relations between human beings and human institutions.

ECT (electroconvulsive therapy): See *shock therapy*.

EEG: See *electroencephalogram*.

ego: In psychoanalytic theory, one of the three major divisions in the model of the psychic apparatus, the others being the *id* and *superego*. The ego represents the sum of certain *mental mechanisms,* such as perception and memory, and specific *defense mechanisms.* The ego serves to mediate between the demands of primitive instinctual drives (the *id*), of internalized parental and social prohibitions (the *superego*), and of reality. The compromises between these forces achieved by the ego tend to resolve intrapsychic conflict and serve an adaptive and executive function. Psychiatric usage of the term should not be confused with common usage, which connotes "self-love" or "selfishness."

ego analysis: Intensive psychoanalytic study and analysis of the ways in which the ego resolves or attempts to deal with intrapsychic conflicts, especially in relation to the development of *mental mechanisms* and the maturation of capacity for rational thought and act. Modern psychoanalysis gives more emphasis to considerations of the defensive operations of the ego than did earlier techniques, which emphasized instinctual forces to a greater degree.

ego-dystonic: Aspects of the individual's behavior, thoughts, and attitudes that he views as repugnant or inconsistent with his total personality. See also *ego-syntonic*.

ego ideal: That part of the personality that comprises the aims and goals of the self; usually refers to the conscious or unconscious emulation of significant figures with whom the person has identified. The ego ideal emphasizes what one should be or do in contrast to what one should not be or do.

egomania: See under *mania*.

ego-syntonic: Aspects of the individual's behavior, thoughts, and attitudes that he views as acceptable and consistent with his total personality. See also *ego-dystonic*.

eidetic image: Unusually vivid and apparently exact mental image; may be a memory, fantasy, or dream.

elaboration: In psychiatry, an unconscious psychologic process of expansion and embellishment of detail, especially with reference to a symbol or representation in a dream.

Electra complex: Obsolescent term. Analogous in the female to *Oedipus complex* (q.v. under *complex*).

electroconvulsive treatment: See *shock therapy*.

electroencephalogram (EEG): A graphic recording of minute electrical impulses arising from activity of cells in the brain. Used in neurologic and psychiatric diagnosis and research.

electroshock therapy (EST): See *electroconvulsive treatment* under *shock therapy*.

electrostimulation: See *electroconvulsive treatment* under *shock therapy*.

elope (elopement): In hospital psychiatry, a term sometimes used for a patient's unauthorized departure from a mental hospital.

emotion: A feeling such as fear, anger, grief, joy, or love. As used in psychiatry, emotions may not always be conscious. Synonymous with *affect.*

emotionally disturbed: Often used to describe a person with a *mental disorder.*

emotional health: Often used synonymously with *mental health.*

emotional illness: Often used synonymously with *mental disorder.*

empathy: An objective and insightful awareness of the feelings, emotions, and behavior of another person, their meaning and significance; to be distinguished from sympathy, which is usually nonobjective and noncritical.

encephalitis: A general term used to designate a diffuse inflammation of the brain. The condition may be acute or chronic and may be caused by a variety of agents such as viruses, bacteria, spirochetes, fungi, protozoa, and chemicals (such as lead). In addition to a number of neurological signs and symptoms, a variety of mental and behavioral changes occur during the illness and may persist beyond the acute phase of the illness. See *encephalopathy, organic brain syndromes.*

encephalopathy: A broad term designating any of the diffuse degenerative diseases of the brain. See *Alzheimer's disease, Pick's disease, encephalitis, Parkinsonism, Huntington's chorea, organic brain syndromes.*

encopresis: Inability to retain feces; incontinence. Cf. *enuresis.*

endocrine disorders: Dysfunction of any of the endocrine glands. Of special concern in psychiatry are those *psychophysiologic disorders* in which dysfunction of the endocrine glands may be caused or aggravated by emotional factors, or which, regardless of etiology, may produce varying degrees of mental and behavioral disturbances.

engram: A memory trace. Theoretically, a change in neural tissue that accounts for persistence of memory.

entropy: In psychiatry, diminished capacity for spontaneous change such as occurs in aging.

enuresis: Bed wetting.

epidemiology: In psychiatry, the study of the incidence, distribution, prevalence, and control of mental disorders in a given population. Common terms used in epidemiology are:

incidence: The number of new cases of a mental disorder that occur in a given population over a set period of time, a year, for example.

epidemic: Describes a disorder or the outbreak of a disorder that affects significant numbers of persons in a given population at any time.

endemic: Describes a disorder that is native to or restricted to a particular area.

pandemic: Describes a disorder that occurs over a very wide area or in many countries, or even universally.

prevalence: The number of cases of a disorder that currently exists in a given population. **Point prevalence:** The number of cases that exists at a specific point in time. **Period prevalence:** The number of cases that exists in a defined period of time. **Lifetime prevalence:** The number of persons who have had a disorder in their lifetimes.

epilepsy: A disorder characterized by periodic motor or sensory seizures or their equivalents, and sometimes accompanied by a loss of consciousness or by certain equivalent manifestations. May be idiopathic (no known organic cause) or symptomatic (due to organic lesions). Usually accompanied by abnormal electrical discharge as shown by EEG. See also *convulsive disorders*.

epileptic equivalent: Episodic, sensory, or motor phenomena which an individual with epilepsy may experience instead of convulsive seizures.

Jacksonian epilepsy: Recurrent episodes of convulsive seizures or spasms localized in a part or region of the body without loss of consciousness. Named after Hughlings Jackson (1835-1911).

major epilepsy (grand mal): Characterized by gross convulsive seizures with loss of consciousness.

minor epilepsy (petit mal): Minor, nonconvulsive epileptic seizures or equivalents; may be limited to only momentary lapses of consciousness.

psychomotor epilepsy: Recurrent periodic disturbances, usually of behavior, during which the patient carries out movements often repetitive, highly organized but semiautomatic in character.

epileptoid personality disorder: See *explosive personality* under *personality disorders.*

epinephrine: One of the *catecholamines* secreted by the adrenal gland and by fibers of the *sympathetic nervous system.* It is responsible for many of the physical manifestations of fear and anxiety. Also known as adrenalin.

erogenous zone: See *erotogenic zone.*

erotic: Consciously or unconsciously invested with sexual feeling; sensually related.

erotogenic zone: An area of the body particularly susceptible to erotic arousal when stimulated, and especially the oral, anal, and genital areas. Sometimes called *erogenous zone.*

erotomania: See *–mania.*

erythrophobia: See under *phobia.*

ESP: See *extra-sensory perception.*

EST (also ECT): See *electroconvulsive treatment.*

ethology: The scientific study of the behavior of animals in their natural habitats. Also the empirical study of human behavior.

etiology: Causation, particularly with reference to disease.

euphoria: An exaggerated feeling of physical and emotional well-being not consonant with apparent stimuli or events;

usually of psychologic origin, but also seen in organic brain diseases, toxic, and drug induced states.

executant ego function: A psychoanalytic term for the ego's management of the *mental mechanisms* in order to meet the needs of the organism. See also *ego*.

exhibitionism: See under *sexual deviation*.

existential psychiatry (existentialism): A school of psychiatry that has evolved out of orthodox psychoanalytic thought and incorporates the ideas of such existentialists as Kierkegaard, Heidigger, Sartre, and others. It focuses on the individual's subjective awareness of his style of existence, his intimate interaction with himself, his values, and his environment. Stress is placed on the way in which man experiences the phenomenological world about him and takes responsibility for his existence. Philosophically, the point of view is *holistic* and self-deterministic in contrast to biologically or culturally deterministic points of view. See also *phenomenology*.

explosive personality: See under *personality disorder*.

extrapsychic: That which takes place between the *psyche* (mind) and the environment.

extrapsychic conflict: See under *conflict*.

extrapyramidal syndrome: A variety of signs and symptoms, including muscular rigidity, tremors, drooling, restlessness, peculiar involuntary movements and postures, shuffling gait, protrusion of the tongue, chewing movements, blurred vision, and many other neurological disturbances. Results from dysfunction of the *extrapyramidal system*. May occur as a reversible side effect of certain psychotropic drugs, particularly *phenothiazines*. *Parkinson's disease* is an irreversible, organically caused manifestation of this syndrome.

extrapyramidal system: The portion of the *central nervous system* responsible for coordinating and integrating various aspects of motor behavior or bodily movements.

extrasensory perception (ESP): Perception without recourse to the conventional use of any of the five physical senses. See also *telepathy*.

extraversion: A state in which attention and energies are largely directed outward from the self, as opposed to inward toward the self, as in *introversion*.

family therapy: Treatment of more than one member of the family simultaneously in the same session. The treatment may be supportive, directive, or interpretive. The assumption is that a mental disorder in one member of a family may be a manifestation of disorder in other members and in their interrelationships and functioning as a total group.

fantasy: An imagined sequence of events or mental images, e.g., day dreams. Serves to express unconscious conflicts, to gratify unconscious wishes, or to prepare for anticipated future events.

fear: Emotional response to recognized sources of danger, to be distinguished from *anxiety*. See *phobia*.

feeblemindedness: Obsolete. See *mental retardation*.

fellatio: Sexual stimulation of the penis by oral contact.

fetish: An inanimate object, such as an article of apparel, symbolically endowed with special meaning. Often necessary for completion of the sexual act.

fetishism: See *sexual deviation*.

fixation: The arrest of psychosexual maturation. Depending on degree it may be either normal or pathological. See *psychosexual development*.

flagellantism: A masochistic or sadistic act in which one or both participants derive stimulation, usually erotic, from whipping or being whipped.

flexibilitas cerea: See *cerea flexibilitas*.

flight of ideas: Verbal skipping from one idea to another. The ideas appear to be continuous but are fragmentary and determined by chance associations. Sometimes seen in manic-depressive illness.

folie à deux: A condition in which two closely related persons, usually in the same family, share the same delusions.

forensic psychiatry: That branch of psychiatry dealing with the legal aspects of mental disorders.

forepleasure: Sexual play preceding intercourse.

formication: In psychiatry, the tactile hallucination or illusion that insects are crawling on the body.

free association: In psychoanalytic therapy, spontaneous, uncensored verbalization by the patient of whatever comes to mind.

free floating anxiety: Severe, generalized, persisting *anxiety*. Often a precursor of *panic*.

Freud, Sigmund (1856-1939): Founder of *psychoanalysis*. Most of the basic concepts of dynamic psychiatry are derived from his theories.

frigidity: Psychogenically inhibited female sexual response manifested by a variety of difficulties ranging from complete lack of sexual response to incomplete orgastic climax.

fugue: A major state of personality dissociation characterized by amnesia; may involve actual physical flight from the customary environment.

functional: In medicine, changes in the way an organ system operates that are not attributed to known structural alterations. While it is true that psychogenic disorders are functional in that their symptoms are not based on any detectable alterations in the structure of the brain or *psyche,* it is not true that all functional disorders of the psyche are of emotional origin any more than functional heart murmurs are based on emotional conflict. A drug-induced, temporary disturbance in central synaptic transmission, for example, may produce psychologic or behavioral abnormalities, but such changes in function are not correctly considered to be psychogenic in origin.

galvanic skin response (GSR): The resistance of the skin to the passage of a weak electric current: an easily measured variable widely used in experimental studies as a measure of an individual's response to emotion-arousing stimuli.

Ganser's syndrome: Sometimes called "nonsense syndrome" or "syndrome of approximate answers" (e.g. "two times two equals about ten"). Commonly used to characterize behavior of prisoners who seek—either consciously or unconsciously—to mislead others regarding their mental state in order to gain an advantage or escape responsibility.

gender identity: Denotes those aspects of appearance and behavior which society attributes to "masculinity" or "femininity." Gender identity is culturally determined and is to be distinguished from sexual identity, which is biologically determined. Such factors as body physique, external genitalia, cultural and parental attitudes and expectations combine to establish gender identity. Arbitrary cultural or group values may cause conflicts about gender identity by labelling certain nonsexual interests and behavior as being "masculine" or "feminine." See also *gender role*.

gender role: The learned roles and images that individuals present to their environment that declare them to be boy or man, or girl or woman. In sense, *gender identity* is what society expects, while *gender role* is what the individual delivers. Usually the two will be congruent; however, they can be in opposition.

general paresis: See *general paralysis*.

general paralysis (general paresis): A chronic *organic brain syndrome* resulting from a chronic syphilitic infection. Occasionally associated with other neurological signs of syphilitic involvement of the nervous system. Detectable with laboratory tests of the blood or spinal fluid.

general systems theory: A theoretical framework that views events from the standpoint of the "systems" involved in the event. Systems are groups of organized interacting components. The behavior of each system is determined by its own structure, by the aggregate characteristics of its component systems ("subsystems"), and by the larger systems ("suprasystems") of which it is a component. Consequently, all systems may be viewed as part of an inter-related hierarchy (e.g. from subatomic particles to whole societies). The value of this theory in psychiatry lies in its emphasis on the *holistic* nature of personality (as compared to mechanistic, stimulus-response, and cybernetic theories, for example) and in its potential for advancing interdisciplinary understanding by integrating concepts about all of the systems, subsystems, and suprasystems that affect human behavior.

genes: The fundamental units of heredity. Composed of *DNA* and arranged in a characteristic linear order on *chromosomes* within cells, they determine the *genotype* of the individual.

genetic: (1) In biology, pertaining to *genes* or to inherited characteristics. (2) In psychiatry, pertaining to the historical development of an individual's psychological attributes or disorders.

genital phase: See under *psychosexual development*.

genotype: The total set of *genes* received by an individual at the time of conception; genetic constitution. The obverse of *phenotype*.

geriatrics: A branch of medicine dealing with the processes and diseases of the aging. Growing interest in the pschological aspects of the aging process has stimulated the growth of "geriatric psychiatry."

Gestalt psychology: A German school of psychology that emphasizes a total perceptual configuration and the interrelations of its component parts.

globus hystericus: An hysterical symptom in which there is a disturbing sensation of a lump in the throat. See also *hysterical neurosis, conversion type* under *neurosis*.

glossolalia: Gibberish speech.

grand mal: See *epilepsy*.

grandiose: In psychiatry, exaggerated belief or claims of one's importance or identity; often manifested by delusions of great wealth, power, or fame.

grief: Normal, appropriate emotional response to an external and consciously recognized loss; it is usually self-limited and gradually subsides within a reasonable time. To be distinguished from *depression*.

gross stress reaction: A term employed for an acute emotional reaction incident to severe environmental stress, as, for example, in military operations, industrial, domestic, or civilian disasters, and other life situations.

group process: A general term for the way a group goes about solving a common problem.

group psychotherapy: Application of psychotherapeutic techniques to a group, including utilization of interactions of members of the group.

group work: Recreational, social, educational, and cultural activities in the community to further the satisfactions and growth of participating group members by providing positive experiences through the group activity programs, interaction with other group members, and interaction of the group with the community. The trained group worker is skilled and knowledgable in individual and group behavior and community relations. Also called "social group work." Not to be confused with *group psychotherapy*.

habeas corpus: A legal document that brings into court a person held in custody (e.g. in a mental hospital) to determine whether the custody is legal.

halfway house: In psychiatry, a specialized residence for mental patients who do not require full hospitalization but who need an intermediate degree of protection and support before returning to fully independent community living.

hallucination: A false sensory perception in the absence of an actual external stimulus. May be induced by emotional and other factors such as drugs, alcohol, and stress. May occur in any of the senses.

hallucinogen: A chemical agent that produces hallucinations.

hallucinosis: A condition in which the patient hallucinates in a state of clear consciousness.

hebephrenia: See *schizophrenia.*

hedonism: In psychiatry, constant seeking of pleasure and avoidance of pain. See also *anhedonia.*

hermaphrodite: An individual who possesses both male and female sexual organs to some degree. Almost invariably one sex is predominant.

histrionic personality disorder: See *hysterical personality* under *personality disorders.*

holistic: In psychiatry, an approach to the study of the individual as a unique entity, rather than as an aggregate of physiological, psychological, and social characteristics.

hemostasis: The maintenance of self-regulating metabolic or psychologic processes which are optimal for comfort and survival.

homosexual panic: An acute and severe attack of anxiety based upon unconscious conflicts involving homosexuality.

homosexuality: See *sexual deviation.*

Horney, Karen (1885-1952): A psychiatrist and psychoanalyst who proposed a theory of neurosis based on an optimistic philosophy of human nature emphasizing the urge toward self-realization and stressing environmental and cultural factors.

Huntington's chorea: An uncommon hereditary and progressively degenerative disease of the *central nervous system.* Onset is in adult life. Characterized by random movements (lurching, jerking) of the entire body and progressive mental deterioration.

hyperkinesis: Increased or excessive muscular activity seen in some neurological conditions, but more frequently in psychiatric disorders, especially in children.

hyperkinetic: Describes a disorder of childhood or adolescence characterized by overactivity, restlessness, distractibility, and short attention span.

hyperventilation: Overbreathing associated with anxiety and marked by reduction of blood carbon dioxide, subjective complaints of light-headedness, faintness, tingling of the extremities, palpitation, and feelings of inability to get enough air.

hypesthesia: A state of diminished sensitivity to tactile stimuli.

hypnagogic: Related to the semiconscious state immediately preceding sleep; sometimes also loosely used as equivalent to "hypnotic" or "sleep-inducing."

hypnagogic hallucinations: *Hallucinations* occurring during the hypnagogic state. Usually of no pathologic significance.

hypnosis: A state of increased receptivity to suggestion and direction, initially induced by the influence of another person.

Often characterized by an altered state of consciousness similar to that observed in spontaneous dissociative conditions. The degree may vary from mild hypersuggestibility to a trance state with complete anesthesia.

hypnotic: Strictly speaking, any agent that induces sleep. While *sedatives* and *narcotics* in sufficient dosage may produce sleep as an incidental effect, the term "hypnotic" is appropriately reserved for drugs employed primarily to produce sleep. See also *addiction, drug dependency, tranquilizer, psychopharmacology.*

hypocondriacal neurosis: See under *neurosis.*

hypnomania: A mild form of manic activity. See also *manic depressive illness.*

hypochondriacal neurosis: See under *neurosis.*

hysterical neurosis, conversion type: See under *neurosis.*

hysterical neurosis, dissociative type: See under *neurosis.*

hysterical personality: See under *personality disorder.*

hysterical psychosis: An unofficial term for an acute situational reaction in an histrionic type of person, usually manifested by the sudden onset of hallucinations, delusions, bizarre behavior, and volatile affect. As so defined, the term includes such exotic disorders as *amok, koro,* and *latah.*

hysterics: Lay term for uncontrollable emotional outbursts.

iatrogenic illness: An illness unwittingly precipitated, aggravated, or induced by the physician's attitude, examination, comments, or treatment.

ICD (ICD-8, ICDA): See *International Classification of Diseases.*

ICT (insulin coma therapy): See *shock treatment.*

id: In Freudian theory, that part of the personality structure which harbors the unconscious instinctive desires and strivings of the individual. See also *ego, superego.*

idealization: A *mental mechanism,* operating consciously or unconsciously, in which the individual overestimates an admired aspect or attribute of another person.

ideas of reference: Incorrect interpretation of casual incidents and external events as having direct reference to one's self. May reach sufficient intensity to constitute *delusions.*

idée fixe: Fixed idea. Loosely used to descrive a compulsive drive, an obsessive idea, or a delusion.

identification: A *defense mechanism,* operating unconsciously, by which an individual endeavors to pattern himself after another. Identification plays a major role in the development of one's personality and specifically of one's *superego.* To be differentiated from imitation, which is a conscious process.

identity crisis: A loss of the sense of the sameness and historical continuity of one's self, and inability to accept or adopt the role the subject perceives as being expected of him by society; often expressed by isolation, withdrawal, extremism, rebellion, and negativity, and typically triggered by a combination of sudden increase in the strength of instinctual drives in a milieu of rapid social evolution and technological change.

idiopathic: Of unknown cause.

idiot: Obsolescent term. See *mental retardation.*

idiot-savant: An individual with gross mental retardation who nonetheless is capable of performing certain remarkable "intellectual" feats such as calendar calculation and puzzle solving.

illusion: The misinterpretation of a real experience.

imago: In Jungian psychology, an unconscious mental image, usually idealized, of an important person in the early history of the individual.

imbecile: Obsolescent term. See *mental retardation.*

impotence: Usually refers to inability of the male to perform the sexual act, generally for psychologic reasons; more broadly used to indicate powerlessness or lack of sexual vigor.

imprinting: A relatively recent term used in *ethology* to refer to a process similar to rapid learning or behavioral patterning that occurs at critical points in very early stages of development in animals. The extent to which imprinting occurs in human development has not been established.

impulse: A psychic striving; usually refers to an instinctive urge.

impulse disorders: An unofficial term for a varied group of nonpsychotic disorders in which impulse control is weak. The impulsive behavior is usually pleasurable, irresistible, and *ego-syntonic.*

inadequate personality: See under *personality disorder.*

incompetent: A legal term for a person who, because of mental defect, cannot be held responsible in certain legal procedures such as making a will, entering into a contract, or standing trial.

incorporation: A primitive *defense mechanism,* operating unconsciously, in which the psychic representation of a person, or parts of him, are figuratively ingested. Example: infantile fantasy that the mother's breast has been ingested and is part of one's self.

individual psychology: The system of psychiatric theory, research, and therapy developed by *Alfred Adler* which stresses *compensation* and *overcompensation* for inferiority feelings.

Indoklon therapy: See *shock therapy.*

indoles: A group of *biogenic amines* derived from tryptophan. Certain of these amines, such as tryptamine and serotonin, exert an important influence on the activity of the *central nervous system.*

industrial psychiatry: See *occupational psychiatry.*

inferiority complex: See *complex.*

information theory: A philosophical system that deals with the mathematical characteristics of communicated messages and the systems that transmit, propagate, distort, or receive them.

inhibition: In psychiatry, an unconscious defense against forbidden instinctual drives; it may interfere with or restrict specific activities or general patterns of behavior.

insanity: A vague, legal term for psychosis, now obsolete in psychiatric usage. Generally connotes: (a) a mental incompetence, (b) inability to distinguish "right from wrong," and/or (c) a condition that interferes with the individual's ability to care for himself or that constitutes a danger to himself or to others. See *Currens Formula, Durham Decision, McNaghten Rule.*

insight: Self-understanding. The extent of the individual's understanding of the origin, nature, and mechanisms of his attitudes and behavior. More superficially, recognition by a patient that he is mentally ill.

instinct: An inborn *drive.* The primary human instincts include self-preservation and sexuality and — for some proponents — *aggression,* the *ego instincts,* and "herd" or "social" instincts. Freud also postulated a *death instinct.*

instrumental conditioning: See under *conditioning.*

insulin coma therapy: See *shock therapy*.

integration: The useful organization and incorporation of both new and old data, experience, and emotional capacities into the personality. Also refers to the organization and amalgamation of functions at various levels of *psychosexual development*.

intellectualization: The *defense mechanism* that utilizes reasoning as a defense against conscious confrontation with unconscious conflicts and their stressful emotions.

intelligence: Capacity to learn and to utilize appropriately what one has learned. May be affected by emotions.

intelligence quotient (IQ): A numerical rating determined through psychological testing that indicates the approximate relationship of a person's mental age (MA) to his chronological age (CA). Expressed mathematically as $IQ = \dfrac{MA}{CA} \times 100$. Thus, if MA=6 and CA=12, then IQ=6/12 × 100 or 50 (retarded). If MA=12 and CA=12, then IQ=100 (average). If MA=18 and CA=12, then IQ=150 (very superior). (Note: Since intellectual capacity is assumed to be fully developed about age 15, adult IQ's are computed by using a fixed arbitrary value of 15 for CA.)

International Classification of Diseases (ICD): The official list of disease categories issued by the World Health Organization. Subscribed to by all WHO member nations, who may assign their own terms to each ICD category. *ICDA* (*International Classification of Diseases, Adapted for Use in the United States*), prepared by the U.S. Public Health Service, represents the official list of diagnostic terms to be used for each ICD category in this country. *DSM-II* is based upon the eighth revision of the International Classification of Diseases (*ICD-8*) prepared in 1966.

interpretation: The process by which the therapist communicates to the patient understanding of a particular aspect of his problems or behavior.

intrapsychic: That which takes place within the *psyche* or mind.

intrapsychic conflict: See under *conflict.*

introjection: A *defense mechanism,* operating unconsciously, whereby loved or hated external objects are taken within oneself symbolically. The converse of *projection.* May serve as a defense against conscious recognition of intolerable hostile impulses. For example, in severe depression, the individual may unconsciously direct unacceptable hatred or aggression toward himself, i.e. toward the introjected object within himself. Related to the more primitive mechanism of *incorporation.*

introversion: Preoccupation with oneself and accompanying reduction of interest in the outside world. Roughly, the reverse of *extraversion.*

involutional melancholia (involutional psychosis): A *major affective disorder* occurring in late middle life and characterized by worry, anxiety, agitation, and severe insomnia. Feelings of guilt and somatic preoccupations are common and may be of delusional proportions.

involutional paranoid state (involutional paraphrenia): See under *paranoid states.*

inward aggression: See under *aggression.*

IQ: See *intelligence quotient.*

irresistible impulse test: A formula that states that a person is not responsible for a crime if his act was compelled by an irresistible impulse. This is usually construed to mean a psychotic or an obsessive-compulsive (neurotic) impulse and not a simple reaction of rage. Currently, the irresistible impulse test is accepted in 14 states, rejected in the remaining 36.

isolation: A *defense mechanism,* operating unconsciously, in which an unacceptable impulse, idea, or act is separated from its original memory source, thereby removing the emotional charge associated with the original memory.

Jacksonian epilepsy: See *epilepsy*.

Janet, Pierre (1859-1947): French psychiatrist. Described *psychasthenia,* which is sometimes referred to as Janet's disease. Also first to use term *la belle indifférence.*

Joint Commission on Mental Health of Children: An agency similar to the *Joint Commission on Mental Illness and Health* (q.v.). Supported by Federal funds, it was established in 1965 to conduct a national study of the mental health needs of children. Its final report was scheduled for publication in 1969.

Joint Commission on Mental Illness and Health: A multi-disciplinary agency, incorporated in 1956, and representing thirty-six national agencies in the mental health and welfare fields. It conducted a five-year study of the mental health needs of the nation between 1956 and 1961 as authorized by the U.S. Congress in the Mental Health Study Act of 1955. The final report of the Joint Commission, *Action for Mental Health,* led ultimately to legislation by the Congress in 1964 authorizing and appropriating funds to facilitate the development of community mental health centers for the mentally ill and mentally retarded in the several states.

Jones, Ernest (1879-1958): Early pupil of Freud and his principal biographer. He pioneered in introducing *psychoanalysis* to the English-speaking world.

Jung, Carl Gustav (1875-1961): Swiss psychoanalyst. Founder of the school of *analytic psychology.*

Kirkbride, Thomas S. (1809-1883): American psychiatrist; one of the founders of the American Psychiatric Association. Noted for his pioneer contributions to mental hospital design.

kleptomania: See *–mania.*

koro: A culture-bound syndrome, this psychogenic disorder is found primarily among the peoples of Indonesia and South China. Koro is an acute anxiety reaction in which the patient feels that his penis is shrinking and will retract into his abdomen causing him to die. Occasionally, comparable anxiety is expressed by females, who complain of shrinking of their breasts and external genitalia.

Korsakov's psychosis: A mental disorder with brain damage characterized by amnesia, compensatory *confabulation,* disturbance of attention, and peripheral neuritis. Usually associated with *alcoholism* and dietary deficiencies.

Kraepelin, Emil (1865-1926): A German psychiatrist who developed an extensive systematic classification of mental diseases. One of the first workers to delineate the concept of *dementia praecox* or *schizophrenia.* See also *descriptive psychiatry.*

la belle indifférence: Literally, "beautiful indifference." Seen in certain patients with hysterical neurosis, conversion type (q.v. under *neurosis*), who show an inappropriate lack of concern about their disabilities.

labile: In psychiatry, pertaining to rapidly shifting emotions; unstable.

lapsus linguae: A slip of the tongue due to unconcious factors.

latah: A culture-bound syndrome seen mostly among Malay-speaking peoples but also observed in the Philippines, Siberia, Lapland, North America, and Africa. Latah is a state of extreme suggestibility and mimicking in response to a sudden stimulus. The subject feels helplessly compelled to imitate any action he sees or repeat any word or sound he hears, regardless of its inappropriateness and unacceptability to him. This psychogenic disorder, with its compulsive *echolalia* and *echopraxia,* is usually relatively brief but may become chronic.

latency period: See under *psychosexual development.*

latent content: The hidden (unconscious) meaning of thoughts or actions, especially in dreams or fantasies. In dreams it is expressed in distorted, disguised, condensed, and symbolic form, which is known as the *manifest content.*

latent homosexuality: See under *sexual deviation.*

laterality: See under *speech disturbance.*

learning disturbance: See under *speech disturbance.*

lesbian: Homosexual woman.

libido: The psychic drive or energy usually associated with the sexual instinct. (Sexual is used here in the broad sense to include pleasure and love-object seeking.)

lithium therapy: The use of certain lithium salts in the treatment of *manic* and *hypomanic* states of excitement. See also *manic-depressive illness.*

lobotomy: See *psychosurgery.*

logorrhea: Uncontrollable, excessive talking.

LSD (lysergic acid diethylamide): An extremely potent drug that produces symptoms and behavior resembling certain psychoses. These symptoms may include *hallucinations, delusions,* and time-space distortions.

lunacy: Obsolete legal term for a major mental illness.

lunatic: Obsolete legal term for a psychotic person.

magical thinking: A person's conviction that thinking equates with doing. Occurs in dreams, in children and primitive peoples, and in patients under a variety of conditions. Characterized by lack of realistic relationship between cause and effect.

major affective disorders: A group of psychoses characterized by severe disorders of mood — either extreme depression or elation or both — that do not seem to be attributable entirely to precipitating life experiences. Includes *involutional melancholia* and the varieties of *manic-depressive illness.*

major epilepsy (grand mal): See under *epilepsy.*

maladjustment: See *adaptation.*

malingering: Deliberate simulation or exaggeration of an illness or disability that, in fact, is nonexistent or minor, in order to avoid an unpleasant situation or to obtain some type of personal gain. See also *compensation neurosis* and *secondary gain.*

—mania: Formerly used as a nonspecific term for any kind of "madness." Currently used as a suffix with any number of Greek roots to indicate a morbid preoccupation with some kind of idea or activity, and/or a compulsive need to behave in some deviant way. *Phobia* as a suffix is used in a similar way. For example, hellenomania, the tendency to use cumbersome Greek or Latin terms instead of readily understandable English words, characterizes the pseudo-erudite jargon of many fields as evidenced by the various terms (often unpreferred) listed below and elsewhere under *phobia.*

dipsomania: Compulsion to drink alcoholic beverages.

egomania: Pathological preoccupation with self.

erotomania: Pathological preoccupation with erotic fantasies or activities.

kleptomania: Compulsion to steal.

megalomania: Pathological preoccupation with delusions of power or wealth.

monomania: Pathological preoccupation with one subject.

necromania: Pathological preoccupation with dead bodies.

nymphomania: Abnormal and excessive need or desire in the female for sexual intercourse. Most nymphomaniacs, if not all, fail to achieve orgasm in the sexual act. See also *erotomania, satyriasis.*

pyromania: Morbid compulsion to set fires..

trichotillomania: Compulsion to pull out one's hair.

mania: A mood disorder characterized by excessive elation, hyperactivity, agitation, and accelerated thinking and speaking, sometimes manifested as *flight of ideas.* Mania is seen most frequently as one of the two major forms of *manic-depressive illness.*

maniac: Imprecise, sensational, and misleading lay term for an emotionally disturbed person. Usually implies violent behavior. Is not specifically referable to any psychiatric diagnostic category.

manic-depressive illness: A *major affective disorder* characterized by severe mood swings and a tendency to remission and recurrence. It is divided into the following three subgroups:

depressed type: A kind of manic-depressive illness consisting exclusively of depressive episodes characterized by severely depressed mood and by mental and motor retardation that may progress to stupor. Uneasiness, apprehension, perplexity, and agitation may also be present.

circular type: A manic-depressive illness distinguished by at least one depressive episode *and* a manic episode.

manic type: A kind of manic-depressive illness consisting exclusively of manic episodes characterized by excessive elation, irritability, talkativeness, *flight of ideas,* and accelerated speech and motor activity.

manifest content: The remembered content of a dream or fantasy, as opposed to *latent content,* which it conceals and distorts.

MAO inhibitor (MAOI): *Monoamine oxidase inhibitor* (q.v.)

masculine protest: Term coined by *Alfred Adler* to describe a striving to escape identification with the feminine role. Applies primarily to women but may also be noted in the male.

masochism: See *sexual deviation.*

maximum security unit: A building or ward in a mental hospital or other institutional setting especially designed to prevent the escape of mental patients who have committed crimes or whose symptoms are a physical threat to the safety of others. See also *criminally insane.*

McNaghten Rule (Also M'Naghten, McNaughten, and Mc-Naughton): The formula that holds a person not responsible for a crime if the accused "was laboring under such a defect of reason from disease of the mind as not to know the nature and quality of the act; or, if he did know it, that he did not know that he was doing what was wrong." This is the criminal responsibility formula in most states of the U.S.A. Also see *Currens Formula, Durham Decision,* and *irresistible impulse.*

megalomania: See *—mania.*

melancholia: See *involutional melancholia.*

menarche: The beginning of menstrual functioning.

mens rea: A guilty intent; that is, an intent to do harm. In a criminal case involving a defendant's mental state an important question may be whether he had *mens rea,* the ability to form an intention to do harm.

mental age: The age level of mental ability determined by standard intelligence tests; distinguished from chronologic age. See *intelligence quotient.*

mental deficiency: See *mental retardation.*

mental disease: See *mental disorder.*

mental disorder: Any psychiatric illness or disease included in the World Health Organization's *International Classification of Diseases,* or in the American Psychiatric Association's *Diagnostic and Statistical Manual of Mental Disorders,* Second Edition (1968). Many of these disorders are defined in this glossary.

mental health: A state of being, relative rather than absolute, in which a person has effected a reasonably satisfactory integration of his instinctual drives. His integration is acceptable to himself and to his social milieu as reflected in his interpersonal relationships, his level of satisfaction in living, his actual achievement, his flexibility, and the level of maturity he has attained.

mental hygiene: Measures employed to reduce the incidence of mental disorders through prevention and early treatment and to promote mental health.

mental illness: Same as *mental disorder.*

mental mechanism: A generic term for a variety of psychic processes that are functions of the *ego* and largely unconscious. Includes *perception,* memory, thinking, and *defense mechanisms.*

mental retardation: Subnormal general intellectual functioning, which may be evident at birth or develop during childhood. Learning, social adjustment, and maturation are impaired. Emotional disturbance is often present. The degree of retardation is commonly measured in terms of IQ: borderline (68-83), mild (52-67), moderate (36-51), severe (20-35), and profound (under 20).

mescaline: An alkaloid originally derived from the peyote cactus, resembling amphetamine and adrenalin chemically; used experimentally to induce hallucinations. Used by Indians of the Southwest in religious rites.

mesmerism: Early term for *hypnosis.* Named after *Anton Mesmer* (1733-1815).

metapsychology: The branch of theoretical or speculative psychology that deals with the significance of mental processes; the nature of the mind-body interrelationship; the origin, purpose, and structure of the mind; and similar hypotheses that are beyond the realm of empirical verification.

Methadone: A synthetic narcotic used to treat patients severely addicted to heroin. In effect, it replaces one addiction with another less socially disabling addiction. See also *narcotic blockade.*

Metrazol shock therapy: See *shock treatment.*

Meyer, Adolf (1866-1950): American psychiatrist, longtime professor of psychiatry at Johns Hopkins University, who formulated and introduced the concept of *psychobiology.*

migraine: A syndrome characterized by recurrent, severe, and usually one-sided headaches, often associated with nausea, vomiting, and visual disturbances. May be related to unconscious emotional conflicts.

milieu therapy: Literally, treatment by environment in a hospital setting. Physical surroundings, equipment, and staff attitudes are structured in such a way as to enhance the effectiveness of other therapies and foster the patient's rehabilitation. See also *total push therapy, therapeutic community.*

minor epilepsy (petit mal): See under *epilepsy.*

Mitchell, S. Weir (1830-1914): American neurologist who described *causalgia* and developed a once popular "rest cure" for emotional disorders.

MMPI (Minnesota Multiphasic Personality Inventory): A questionnaire type of psychological test designed for persons sixteen years of age and over. It may be administered individually or in groups. Although the MMPI has certain limitations, as a self-reporting test it is one of the most carefully validated and reliable instruments of its kind.

mongolism: Archaic term for *Down's syndrome.*

monoamine oxidase inhibitor (MAOI): A group of antidepressant drugs that appear to ameliorate the emotional state by inhibiting certain brain enzymes and raising the level of *serotonin.*

monomania: See *–mania.*

moral treatment: A philosophy and technique of treating mental hospital patients that prevailed in the first half of the nineteenth century. It emphasized removal of restraints, humane and kindly care, attention to religion, and performance of useful tasks in the hospital. Historically, the antecedent of the modern *therapeutic community* and *milieu therapy.*

moron: Obsolescent term for an individual with borderline or mild *mental retardation.*

multiple personality: A term used by *Morton Prince* for a rare type of dissociative reaction in which the individual adopts two or more different personalities. These are separate and compartmentalized, with total amnesia for the one, or ones, not in awareness.

mutation: In biology, a change in hereditary constitution that causes genetically transmissable permanent differences between the characteristics of an individual and those of his parents; may occur spontaneously or may be induced by such agents as high-energy radiation. See also *genes.*

mutism: In psychiatry, refusal to speak for conscious or unconscious reasons. Often seen in *psychosis.*

mysophobia: See under *phobia.*

narcissism (narcism): From Narcissus, figure in Greek mythology who fell in love with his own reflected image. Self-love, as opposed to object-love (love of another person). In psychoanalytic theory, cathexis (investment) of the psychic representation of the self with libido (sexual interest and energy). Some degree of narcissism is considered healthy and normal, but an excess interferes with relations with others. To be distinguished from egotism, which carries the connotation of self-centeredness, selfishness, and conceit. Egotism is but one expression of narcissism. See also *cathexis,* and *libido.*

narcoanalysis: See *narcosynthesis.*

narcolepsy: Brief, uncontrollable episodes of sleeping.

narcosis: *Stupor,* of varying depth, induced by certain drugs.

narcosynthesis: Psychotherapeutic treatment under partial anesthesia, e.g. as induced by sodium amytal or pentothal. Originally used to treat acute mental disorders caused by military combat.

narcotic: Any drug, natural or synthetic, that produces sleep or even *stupor* and relieves pain. See *addiction, drug dependency, hypnotic, sedative.*

narcotic blockade: Total or partial inhibition of the euphoria produced by narcotic drugs through the use of other drugs, such as *Methadone,* which can then be used as maintenance treatment without producing the peaks of elation, *withdrawal symptoms,* and demand for increasing dosage that characterize addiction to opiates.

National Association for Mental Health: Leading voluntary citizens' organization in the mental health field. Founded in 1909 by *Clifford W. Beers* as the National Committee for Mental Hygiene.

National Institute of Mental Health: A government bureau within the U.S. Department of Health, Education, and Welfare responsible for administering federal grant programs to advance and support mental health research, training, and service programs.

necromania: See *mania.*

negative feelings: In psychiatry, unfriendly, hostile feelings.

negativism: Perverse opposition and resistance to suggestions or advice. Often observed in people who subjectively feel "pushed around." Seen normally in late infancy. A common symptom in *catatonic schizophrenia* (q.v. under *schizophrenia*).

neologism: A new word or condensed combination of several words coined by a person to express a highly complex idea often related to his conflicts; not readily understood by others; common in *schizophrenia.*

neoplasm: A new growth or tumor. Neoplasms that affect behavior are primarily, but not exclusively, found within the cranial cavity. Such neoplasms may cause mental and behavioral disturbances in addition to neurological signs and symptoms. See *organic brain syndromes.*

nervous breakdown: A nonmedical, nonspecific term; a euphemism for a mental disorder.

neurasthenic neurosis (neurasthenia): See under *neurosis.*

neurologist: A physician with postgraduate training and experience in the field of organic diseases of the nervous system and whose professional work focuses primarily in this area.

neurology: The branch of medical science devoted to the study, diagnosis, and treatment of organic diseases of the nervous system.

neuropsychiatry: Combination of the specialties of neurology and psychiatry.

neuroleptic: A synonym for major tranquilizers. (q.v. under *tranquilizer*).

neurosis (psychoneurosis): An emotional maladaption characterized chiefly by anxiety arising from some unresolved unconscious conflicts. This anxiety is either felt directly or controlled by various psychological mechanisms to produce other, subjectively distressing symptoms. The neuroses are usually considered less severe than the psychoses (although not always less disabling) because they manifest neither gross personality disorganization nor gross distortion or misinterpretation of external reality. The neuroses are classified according to the predominating symptoms. The common neuroses are:

anxiety neurosis: A neurosis characterized by anxious over-concern occasionally progressing to panic; frequently associated with somatic symptoms.

depersonalization neurosis: A neurosis characterized by feelings of unreality and of estrangement from the self, body, or surroundings. Different from the process of *depersonalization,* which may be a manifestation of normal anxiety or of another mental disorder.

depressive neurosis: A neurosis manifested by an excessive reaction of depression due to an internal conflict or to an identifiable event, such as a loss of a loved person or a cherished possession.

hypochondriacal neurosis: A neurosis characterized by preoccupation with the body and with fear of presumed diseases of various organs. Although the fears are not delusional in quality, they persist despite reassurance.

hysterical neurosis: A neurosis characterized by a sudden psychogenic loss or disorder of function in response to an emotional stress. This disorder is divided into two subtypes:

conversion type: An hysterical neurosis manifested by disorders of the special senses or the voluntary nervous system, such as blindness, deafness, *anesthesia, paresthesia,* paralysis, and impaired muscular coordination. A patient with this disorder may show *la belle indifférence* about his symptoms, which may actually provide *secondary gains* by winning him sympathy or relieving him of unpleasant responsibilities. See also *conversion.*

dissociative type: An hysterical neurosis manifested by alterations in the patient's state of consciousness or in his identity, producing such symptoms as *amnesia, somnambulism, fugue,* or *multiple personality.* See also *dissociation.*

neurasthenic neurosis (neurasthenia): A neurosis characterized by complaints of chronic weakness, easy fatigability, and exhaustion.

obsessive compulsive neurosis: A neurosis characterized by the persistent intrusion of unwanted thoughts, urges, or actions that the individual is unable to stop. The thoughts may consist of single words or ideas, ruminations, or trains of thought that the individual often views as nonsensical. The actions may vary from simple movements to complex rituals, such as repeated handwashing. See also *compulsion.*

phobic neurosis: A neurosis characterized by intense fear of an object or situation that the individual consciously recognizes as harmless. His apprehension may be experienced as faintness, fatigue, palpations, perspiration, nausea, tremor, and even panic. See also *phobia.*

night hospital: See under *partial hospitalization.*

nihilism: In psychiatry, the delusion of nonexistence of the self or part of the self.

norepinephrine: The neurohormone of the peripheral sympathetic nervous system. A *catecholamine* related to *epinephrine.* Also known as noradrenalin.

nosology: Medical science of classification of diseases.

NREM sleep: See *REM Sleep*.

nymphomania: See *–mania*.

object relations: The emotional bonds that exist between an individual and another person, as contrasted with his interest in, and love for, himself; usually described in terms of his capacity for loving and reacting appropriately to others.

obsession: A persistent, unwanted idea or impulse that cannot be eliminated by logic or reasoning.

obsessive compulsive neurosis: See under *neurosis*.

obsessive compulsive personality: See under *personality disorder*.

occupational psychiatry: A field of psychiatry concerned with the diagnosis and prevention of mental illness in industry and with psychiatric aspects of absenteeism, accident proneness, personnel policies, operational fatigue, vocational adjustment, retirement, and related phenomena.

occupational therapy: An adjunctive therapy that utilizes purposeful activities as a means of altering the course of illness. The patient's relationship to staff personnel and to other patients in the occupational therapy setting is often more therapeutic than the activity itself.

Oedipus complex: See under *complex*.

oligophrenia: A term for *mental retardation*.

onanism: Incomplete sexual relations with withdrawal just prior to emission. Coitus interruptus. Incorrectly used as a synonym for masturbation.

ontogenetic: Pertaining to the biological development of the individual. Distinguished from *phylogenetic.*

open hospital: Literally, a mental hospital, or section thereof, that has no locked doors or other forms of physical restraint.

operant conditioning: See *conditioning.*

oral phase: See *psychosexual development.*

organic brain syndrome (OBS): A disorder caused by or associated with impairment of brain tissue function. It may be manifested by disorientation, loss of memory, and impairment of the ability to learn, comprehend, calculate, and exercise judgment. May be psychotic or nonpsychotic, mild, moderate, or severe. Simple drunkenness is an example of nonpsychotic OBS, and *senile dementia* of the psychotic type.

organic disease: A disease characterized by significant demonstrable structural or biochemical abnormality in an organ or tissue. Sometimes imprecisely used as an antonym for *functional* illness.

organic psychosis: A severe psychiatric disorder resulting from a demonstrable physical disturbance of brain function such as a tumor, infection, or injury. Characterized by impaired memory, orientation, intelligence, judgment, and mood. See also *psychosis,* and *organic brain syndrome.*

orientation: Awareness of oneself in relation to time, place, and person.

orienting reflex (OR): Pavlovian term used to describe response to a novel stimulus which is not sufficiently strong to elicit a specific inborn *unconditioned reflex* and to which an individual has not learned to produce a conditioned reflex. Turning of the head, focusing of the eyes or ears to a nonspecific noise, light, or touch are examples. See *conditioning.*

orthopsychiatry: An approach to the study and treatment of human behavior that involves the collaborative effort of psychiatry, psychology, psychiatric social work, and other behavioral, medical, and social sciences in the study and treatment of human behavior in the clinical setting. Emphasis is placed on preventive techniques to promote healthy emotional growth and development, particularly of children.

overcompensation: A conscious or unconscious process in which a real or fancied physical or psychologic deficit inspires exaggerated correction.

overdetermination: In psychiatry, a term indicating the multiple causality of a single emotional reaction or symptom. Thus, a single symptom expresses the confluence and condensation of unconscious drives and needs as well as the defenses against them.

overt homosexuality: See under *sexual deviation.*

panic: In psychiatry, an attack of acute, intense, and overwhelming anxiety, accompanied by a considerable degree of personality disorganization. See *anxiety.*

panphobia: See under *phobia.*

paranoia: See under *paranoid states.*

paranoid: An adjective applied to individuals who are oversuspicious, some of whom may also harbor grandiose or persecutory *delusions,* or *ideas of reference.*

paranoid personality: See under *personality disorder.*

paranoid states: Psychotic disorders in which a delusion, generally persecutory or grandiose, is the essential abnormality and accounts for disturbances in mood, behavior, and thinking (including *hallucinations*) that may be present. Its two major subdivisions are:

involutional paranoid state (involutional paraphrenia): A paranoid psychosis characterized by delusion formation that begins in the involutional period. Distinguished from *schizophrenia, paranoid type,* by the absence of a schizophrenic thought disorder.

paranoia: An extremely rare condition characterized by the gradual development of an intricate, complex, and elaborate paranoid system based on (and often proceeding logically from) misinterpretation of an actual event. Frequently the individual considers himself endowed with unique and superior ability. In spite of a chronic course, this condition does not seem to interfere with the rest of the individual's thinking and personality. To be distinguished from *schizophrenia, paranoid type,* and involutional *paranoid state.*

paraphasia: See *speech disturbance.*

paraphrenia: A *paranoid state* consisting of a persecutory or grandiose delusional system without the primary disturbances of thinking and affect that characterize *schizophrenia, paranoid type.* See also *involutional paranoid state* under *paranoid states.*

parapraxis: A faulty act, blunder or lapse of memory such as a slip of the tongue or misplacement of an article. According to Freud, these acts are caused by unconscious motives.

parapsychology: The study of metapsychic (psi) phenomena, i.e., events caused or perceived without the ordinary use of physical actions or senses. Example: predicting outcome of throw of dice. See also *psychokinesis* and *extrasensory perception (ESP).*

parasympathetic nervous system: That part of the *autonomic nervous system* that controls the life-sustaining organs of the body under normal, danger-free conditions. See also *sympathetic nervous system.*

parataxic distortion: Sullivan's term for certain distortions in judgment and perception, particularly in interpersonal relations, based upon the observer's need to perceive subjects and relationships in accordance with a pattern set by earlier experience. Parataxic distortions develop as a defense against anxiety. See *Sullivan.*

paresis: Weakness of organic origin; incomplete paralysis; term often used instead of *general paresis.*

paresthesia: Abnormal tactile sensation. Often described as burning, pricking, tickling, tingling, or creeping. May be hallucinatory in certain psychoses or a manifestation of neurological disease.

Parkinson's disease: See *extrapyramidal syndrome.*

parole: In psychiatry, technical term for the conditional release of a patient from a mental hospital prior to formal discharge so that the patient may be returned to the hospital if necessary without legal action. Obsolescent because of its association with parole from prison. Similar in meaning to "trial visit," "on leave," and "home leave."

partial hospitalization: A psychiatric treatment program for patients who require hospitalization but not on a full-time basis. For example:

> **day hospital:** A special facility or an arrangement within a hospital setting that enables the patient to come to the hospital for treatment during the day and return home at night.

> **night hospital:** A hospital or hospital service for patients who are able to work or otherwise function in the community during the day but who require specialized treatment and supervision in a hospital setting after working hours.

> **weekend hospital:** A hospital setting providing a treatment program over weekends. The patient resumes his usual work and activities outside the hospital during the week.

passive-aggressive personality: See under *personality disorder.*

passive-dependent personality: A disorder manifested by marked indecisiveness, emotional dependency, and lack of self-confidence. For diagnostic purposes, once considered to be a subtype of *passive-aggressive personality*. See under *personality disorders*.

pastoral counseling: The use of psychological principles by clergymen in interviews with parishioners who seek help with emotional problems.

pathognomic: A medical term applied to a symptom or group of symptoms that are specifically diagnostic or typical of a disease entity.

Pavlov, Ivan Petrovich (1849-1936): Russian neurophysiologist noted for his research in *conditioning*. Awarded Nobel Prize in Medicine (1904) for his work on the physiology of digestion.

pavor nocturnus: Nightmare.

pederasty: See *sexual deviation*.

pedophilia: See *sexual deviation*.

pellagra: A specific vitamin deficiency disease that manifests major mental symptoms, such as *delusions* and impaired thinking. It is correctable by treatment with vitamin B_3 (nicotinamide).

penis envy: Literally, envy by the female of the penis of the male. More generally, the female wish for male attributes, position, or advantages. Believed by many to be a significant factor in female character development.

perception: The *mental mechanism* by which the nature and meaning of sensory stimuli are recognized and interpreted by comparing them with stimuli associated with past experiences.

perseveration: Involuntary and pathological persistence of a single response or idea in reply to various questions. Seen most often in organic brain disease.

persona: A Jungian term for the personality "mask" or facade that each person presents to the outside world. Distinguished from the person's inner being or *anima* (q.v.). See also *Jung*.

personality: The characteristic way in which a person behaves; the deeply ingrained pattern of behavior that each person evolves, both consciously and unconsciously, as his style of life or way of being in adapting to his environment. See *adaptation, character disorder, personality disorder.*

personality disorders: A group of mental disorders characterized by deeply ingrained maladaptive patterns of behavior, generally life-long in duration and consequently often recognizable by the time of adolescence or earlier. Affecting primarily the personality of the individual, they are different in quality from *neurosis* and *psychosis.*

antisocial personality: A personality disorder characterized by a basic lack of socialization and by behavior patterns that bring the individual repeatedly into conflict with society. People with this disorder are incapable of significant loyalty to individuals, groups, or social values and are grossly selfish, callous, irresponsible, impulsive, and unable to feel guilt or to learn from experience and punishment. Frustration tolerance is low. Such individuals tend to blame others or offer plausible rationalizations for their behavior.

asthenic personality: A personality disorder characterized by easy fatigability, low energy level, lack of enthusiasm, marked incapacity for enjoyment, and over-sensitivity to physical and emotional stress.

cyclothymic personality (affective personality): A personality disorder characterized by recurring and alternating periods of depression and elation not readily attributable to external circumstances.

explosive personality: A personality disorder characterized by gross outbursts of rage or of verbal or physical aggressiveness. Outbursts are strikingly different from the individual's usual behavior, and he may be regretful and repentant for them. See also *aggression.*

hysterical personality (histrionic personality disorder): A personality disorder characterized by excitability, emotional instability, over-reactivity, and self-dramatization that is attention-seeking and often seductive, whether or not the individual is aware of its purpose. Often individuals with this disorder are immature, self-centered, vain, and unusually dependent on others.

inadequate personality: A personality disorder characterized by ineffectual responses to emotional, social, intellectual, and physical demands. While the individual seems neither physically nor mentally deficient, he does manifest inadaptibility, ineptness, poor judgment, social instability, and lack of physical and emotional stamina.

obsessive compulsive personality (anankastic personality): A personality disorder characterized by excessive concern with conformity and adherence to standards of conscience. Individuals with this disorder may be rigid, over-inhibited, over-conscientious, over-dutiful, indecisive, perfectionistic, and unable to relax easily.

paranoid personality: A personality disorder characterized by hypersensitivity, rigidity, unwarranted suspicion, jealousy, envy, excessive self-importance, and a tendency to blame others and ascribe evil motives to them.

passive-aggressive personality: A personality disorder characterized by aggressive behavior manifested in passive ways, such as obstructionism, pouting, procrastination, intentional inefficiency, or stubbornness. The aggression often arises from resentment at failing to find gratification in a relationship with an individual or institution upon which the individual is over-dependent.

schizoid personality: A personality disorder manifested by shyness, over-sensitivity, seclusiveness, frequent daydreaming, avoidance of close or competitive relationships, and often eccentricity. Individuals with this condition often react to disturbing experiences and conflicts with apparent detachment and are often unable to express hostility and ordinary aggressive feelings.

persuasion: In psychiatry, a therapeutic approach based on direct suggestion and guidance intended to influence favorably patients' attitudes, behavior, and goals.

perversion: Any *sexual deviation*.

petit mal: See *epilepsy*.

phallic phase: See under *psychosexual development*.

phantom limb: A phenomenon frequently experienced by amputees, in which sensations, often painful, appear to originate in the amputated extremity.

phenomenology: The study of occurrences or happenings in 'their own right, rather than from the point of view of inferred causes; specifically, the theory that behavior is determined, not by external reality as it can be described objectively in physical terms, but rather by the way in which the subject perceives that reality at any moment. See *existentialism.*

phenothiazine derivatives: A group of *psychotropic* drugs that, chemically, have in common the phenothiazine nucleus but that differ from one another through variations in chemical structure. As a group of drugs, the phenothiazines are also known as *major tranquilizers* possessing marked antianxiety and antipsychotic properties. See *psychopharmacology* and the other terms listed there.

phenotype: The observable attributes of an individual; the physical manifestations of his *genotype* (q.v.)

phenylketonuria: See *PKU.*

phenylpyruvic oligophrenia: See *PKU.*

phobia: An obsessive, persistent, unrealistic intense fear of an object or situation. The fear is believed to arise through a process of displacing an internal (unconscious) conflict to an external object symbolically related to the conflict. (See also *displacement.*) Some of the common phobias are:

acrophobia: Fear of heights.

agoraphobia: Fear of open places.

ailurophobia: Fear of cats.

algophobia: Fear of pain.

claustrophobia: Fear of closed spaces.

erythrophobia: Fear of blushing; sometimes used to refer to the blushing itself.

mysophobia: Fear of dirt and germs.

panphobia: Fear of everything.

xenophobia: Fear of strangers.

phobic neurosis: See under *neurosis.*

phrenology: Abandoned theory of relationship between bony structure of the skull and mental traits.

phylogenetic: Pertaining to the evolutionary or racial history of the species. See also *ontogenetic.*

pica: A craving for unnatural food; a perverted appetite. Example: children eating plaster or dirt. Seen in hysteria, pregnancy, and emotional disturbances in children.

Pick's disease: A presenile degenerative disease of the brain affecting the cerebral cortex, particularly the frontal lobes. Symptoms include intellectual deterioration, emotional instability, and loss of social adjustment. See also *Alzheimer's disease.*

Pinel, Phillipe (1746-1826): French physician-reformer who pioneered in abolishing the use of restraints in the care of the mentally ill.

PKU (phenylketonuria): A congenital metabolic disturbance characterized by an inability to convert phenylalanine to tyrosine. Results in the abnormal accumulation of chemicals that interfere with brain development. Transmitted genetically. Treatable by diet when detected in infancy. Detectable by testing the urine for the presence of phenylpyruvic acid. If untreated, mental retardation results. Also known as *phenylpyruvic oligophrenia.*

placebo: Originally, an inactive substance such as a "bread pill" given to "placate" a patient who demands medication that is not necessary. Useful in research and practice because of its potential psychological effect, which may be neutral, therapeutic, or noxious depending on suggestion by the therapist or experimenter and the patient's own expectations, faith, fear, apprehension, or hostility. In British usage a placebo is sometimes called a "dummy."

play therapy: A treatment technique utilizing the child's play as a medium for expression and communication between patient and therapist.

pleasure principle: The psychoanalytic concept that man instinctually seeks to avoid pain and discomfort and strives for gratification and pleasure. In personality development theory the pleasure principle antedates and subsequently comes in conflict with the *reality principle* (q.v.).

polyphagia: Pathological overeating.

porphyria: A metabolic disorder characterized by the excretion of porphyrins in the urine and accompanied by attacks of abdominal pain, peripheral neuropathy, and a variety of mental symptoms.

positive feeling: In psychiatry, warm, friendly feelings, as opposed to negative, hostile feelings.

portpartum psychosis: A psychotic episode, usually schizophrenic in nature, following childbirth. Organic or toxic factors may be responsible.

potency: In psychiatry, the male's ability to carry out sexual relations. Often used to refer specifically to the capacity to have and maintain adequate erection of the penis during sexual intercourse.

preconscious: Referring to thoughts that are not in immediate awareness but that can be recalled by conscious effort.

prefrontal lobotomy: A type of *psychosurgery*.

pregenital: In psychoanalysis, refers to the period of early childhood before the genitals have begun to exert the predominant influence in the organization or patterning of sexual behavior. Oral and anal influences predominate during this period. See also *anal erotism* and *oral phase* under *psychosexual development*.

prevention (preventive psychiatry): In traditional medical usage, the prevention or prophylaxis of a disorder. The modern trend, particularly in *community psychiatry,* is to broaden the meaning of prevention to encompass also the amelioration, control, and limitation of disease. Prevention is often categorized as follows:

> **primary prevention:** Measures to prevent a mental disorder, (e.g. preventing *general paralysis* with adequate doses of penicillin in treating syphilis).

secondary prevention: Measures to limit a disease process, (e.g. through early case finding and treatment).

tertiary prevention: Measures to reduce impairment or disability following a disorder, (e.g. through rehabilitation programs).

primal scene: In psychoanalytic theory, the real or fancied observation by the infant of parental or other heterosexual intercourse.

primary gain: The relief from emotional conflict and the freedom from anxiety achieved by a *defense mechanism*. The concept is that mental states, both normal and pathological, develop defensively in largely unconscious attempts to cope with or to resolve unconscious conflicts. All *mental mechanisms* operate in the service of the primary gain, and the need for such gain may be thought of as responsible for the initiation of an emotional illness. To be distinguished from *secondary gain*.

primary process: In psychoanalytic theory, the generally unorganized mental activity characteristic of unconscious mental life. Seen in less disguised form in infancy and in dreams. It is marked by the free discharge of energy and excitation without regard to the demands of environment, reality, or logic. See also *secondary process*.

Prince, Morton (1854-1929): American psychiatrist and neurologist known for his work on *multiple personalities*.

prison psychosis: Term for emotional reactions of psychotic depth precipitated by actual or anticipated incarceration.

privilege: The legal right of a patient, always established by statute, to prevent his physician from testifying about information gleaned in the course of his treatment by the physician. Thus, a legal affirmation of the ethical principle of *confidentiality*. Many states have privileged communication laws.

privileged communication: A legal term for information that a patient discloses to his physician while the latter attends him in a professional capacity. The information is termed "privileged" because in some states by law, and universally according to medical ethics, the physician is not allowed to divulge such information without the patient's consent. Also, the medical record of a patient is regarded as a privileged communication in jurisdictions where privilege is established by law, and in any case, as a *confidential* communication where it is not.

process schizophrenia: See under *schizophrenia.*

projection: A *defense mechanism,* operating unconsciously, whereby that which is emotionally unacceptable in the self is unconsciously rejected and attributed (projected) to others.

projective tests: Psychological tests used as a diagnostic tool in which the test material is so unstructured that any response will reflect a projection of some aspect of the subject's underlying personality and psychopathology. Among the most common projective tests are the *Rorschach* (inkblot) and the *Thematic Apperception Test (TAT).*

psychasthenia: Largely obsolete term introduced by *Janet* to include obsessions, compulsions, doubts, feelings of inadequacy, and phobias. See also *neurasthenia.*

psyche: The mind.

psychedelic: A term applied to any of several drugs that may induce hallucinations and psychotic states, including the production of bizarre distortion of time, sound, color, etc. Among the more commonly used psychedelics are *LSD, marijuana, mescaline,* morning-glory seeds, psilocybin.

psychiatric illness: See *mental disorders.*

psychiatrist: A doctor of medicine who specializes in *psychiatry.*

psychiatry: The medical science that deals with the origin, diagnosis, prevention, and treatment of mental disorders.

psychic determinism: See *determinism.*

psychic energizer: A popular term for drugs that stimulate or elevate the mood of a depressed patient.

psychoanalysis: A psychologic theory of human development and behavior, a method of research, and a system of psychotherapy, originally developed by Sigmund Freud.

Through analysis of free associations and interpretation of dreams, emotions and behavior are traced to the influence of repressed instinctual drives and defenses against them in the unconscious. Psychoanalytic treatment seeks to eliminate or diminish the undesirable effects of unconscious conflicts by making the patient aware of their existence, origin, and inappropriate expression in current emotions and behavior.

psychoanalyst: A psychiatrist who has had additional training in psychoanalysis and who employs the techniques of psychoanalytic therapy.

psychobiology: The science of the human being as an integrated unit. Specifically, it views the individual not as having a psychological and a biological set of functions, but rather as functioning as an integrated unit. Generally associated with *Adolf Meyer,* who introduced the term in the United States in 1915.

psychodrama: A technique of group psychotherapy in which individuals dramatize their emotional problems.

psychodynamics: The systematized knowledge and theory of human behavior and its motivation, the study of which depends largely upon the functional significance of emotion. Psychodynamics recognizes the role of unconscious motivation in human behavior. It is a predictive science, based on the assumption that a person's total make-up and probable reactions at any given moment are the product of past interactions between his specific genetic endowment and the environment in which he has lived from conception onward.

psychogenesis: Production or causation of a symptom or illness by mental or psychic factors as opposed to organic ones.

psychokinesis: The belief that directed thought processes can influence an event such as a throw of dice. See also *parapsychology* and *extrasensory perception (ESP)*.

psycholinguistics: The study of factors affecting activities involved in communicating and comprehending verbal information.

psychologist: One who specializes in psychology. Generally holds a Ph.D. or M.A. degree.

psychologist, clinical: A psychologist with a graduate degree, usually a Ph.D., and with additional supervised training and experience in a clinical setting, who specializes in the evaluation and psychological treatment of mental disorders. Frequently clinical psychologists work in medical settings in collaboration with psychiatrists and other physicians.

psychology: An academic discipline, a profession, and a science dealing with the study of mental processes and behavior in man and animals. See also *psychiatry*.

psychology, analytic: See *analytic psychology* and *Jung*.

psychology, individual: See *individual psychology* and *Adler*.

psychometry: The science of testing and measuring mental and psychologic ability, efficiency, potentials, and functioning, including psychopathologic components. An example is the Stanford-Binet test for intelligence.

psychomotor epilepsy: See under *epilepsy*.

psychomotor excitement: Generalized physical and emotional overactivity in response to internal and/or external stimuli as in hypomania.

psychomotor retardation: A generalized retardation of physical and emotional reactions. The opposite of *psychomotor excitement*.

psychoneurosis: See *neurosis*.

psychoneurotic disorders: See *neurosis*.

psychopathic personality: An informal term for *anti-social personality*. Afflicted individuals are referred to casually as "psychopaths."

psychopathology: The study of the significant causes and processes in the development of mental illness. Also the manifestations of mental illness.

psychopharmacology: The study of the mental and behavioral effects of certain drugs. Some of the many facets of psychopharmacology are described in this glossary under the following terms: *antidepressant, ataractic, neuroleptic, psychedelic, psychic energizer, psychotomimetic, psychotropic, tranquilizer.*

psychophysiologic disorders: A group of disorders characterized by physical symptoms that are caused by emotional factors and that involve a single organ system, usually under *autonomic nervous system* control. Symptoms are caused by physiological changes that normally accompany certain emotional states, but in these disorders the changes are more intense and sustained. Frequently called "psychosomatic disorders." These disorders are usually named and classified according to the organ system involved (e.g. musculo-skeletal, respiratory).

psychosexual development: In psychoanalysis, a term encompassing the various stages of libidinal maturation from infancy to adulthood. The way in which a child experiences these stages significantly influences his basic personality characteristics in later life. The stages are:

oral phase: The earliest of the stages of infantile psychosexual development, lasting from birth to 12 months or longer. Usually subdivided into two stages: the **oral erotic,** relating to the pleasurable experience of sucking; and the **oral sadistic,** associated with aggressive biting. Both oral erotism and sadism continue into adult life in disguised and sublimated forms.

anal phase: The period of pregenital psychosexual development, usually from one to three years, in which the child has particular interest and concern with the process of defecation and the sensations connected with the anus. The pleasurable part of the experience is termed *anal erotism.* See also *anal character.*

phallic phase: The period from about two and a half to six years during which sexual interest, curiosity, and pleasurable experience center about the penis, and in girls, to a lesser extent, the clitoris.

latency period: The period from about five to seven years to adolescence when there is an apparent cessation of psychosexual development.

genital phase: The culminating stage of development in which a person achieves a genuinely affectionate, mature relationship with a sex partner.

psychosis: A major mental disorder of organic or emotional origin in which the individual's ability to think, respond emotionally, remember, communicate, interpret reality, and behave appropriately is sufficiently impaired so as to interfere grossly with his capacity to meet the ordinary demands of life. Often characterized by regressive behavior, inappropriate mood, diminished impulse control, and such abnormal mental content as delusions and hallucinations. The term is applicable to conditions having a wide range of severity and duration. See also *schizophrenia, manic-depressive illness, reactive depression, involutional melancholia,* and *organic brain syndrome.*

psychosomatic: Adjective to denote the constant and inseparable interaction of the *psyche* (mind) and the *soma* (body). Most commonly used to refer to illnesses in which the manifestations are primarily physical with at least a partial emotional etiology. See also *psychophysiologic disorders.*

psychosurgery: Treatment of chronic, severe, and intractable psychiatric disorders by surgical removal or interruption of certain areas or pathways in the brain, especially in the prefrontal lobes.

psychotherapy: The generic term for any type of treatment that is based primarily upon verbal or nonverbal communication with the patient as distinguished from the use of drugs, surgery, or physical measure such as electroconvulsive treatment. The basic treatment method used by psychiatrists either alone or in conjunction with other forms of treatment. See also *psychoanalysis, group therapy.*

psychotic depressive reaction: A psychosis distinguished by a depressive mood attributed to some experience. It is *not* considered one of the *major affective disorders* (q.v.).

psychotomimetic: Literally, mimicking a psychosis. Used to refer to certain drugs such as *LSD* (lysergic acid diethlyamide) or *mescaline*, which produce psychotic states.

psychotropic: A term used to describe drugs that have a special action upon the *psyche.* See *psychopharmacology* and the other terms listed there.

puerperal psychosis: See *postpartum psychosis.*

pyromania: See *–mania.*

q-sort: A personality assessment technique in which the subject (or someone who observes him) indicates the degree to which a standardized set of descriptive statements actually describe the subject. The term reflects the "sorting" procedures occasionally used with this technique.

rapport: In psychiatry, the conscious feeling of harmonious accord, mutual responsiveness, and sympathy that contributes to the patient's confidence in the therapist and willingness to work cooperatively with him. To be distinguished from *transference,* which is unconscious.

rationalization: A *defense mechanism,* operating unconsciously, in which the individual attempts to justify or make consciously tolerable, by plausible means, feelings, behavior and motives that would otherwise be intolerable. Not to be confused with conscious evasion or dissimulation. See also *projection.*

Ray, Isaac (1807-1881): A founder of the American Psychiatric Association whose *Treatise on the Medical Jurisprudence of Insanity* was the pioneer American work in this field.

reaction formation: A *defense mechanism,* operating unconsciously, wherein attitudes and behavior are adopted that are the opposites of impulses the individual harbors either consciously or unconsciously (e.g., excessive moral zeal may be a reaction to strong but repressed asocial impulses).

reactive depression: An informal term for *depressive neurosis.*

reactive schizophrenia: See under *schizophrenia.*

reality principle: In psychoanalytic theory, the concept that the *pleasure principle,* which represent the claims of instinctual wishes, is normally modified by the inescapable demands and requirements of the external world. In fact, the reality principle may still work in behalf of the pleasure principle; but it reflects compromises in the nature of the gratification and allows for the postponement of gratification to a more appropriate time. The reality principle usually becomes more prominent in the course of development but may be weak in certain psychiatric illnesses and undergo strengthening during treatment.

recall: The process of bringing a memory into consciousness. In psychiatry, recall is often used to refer to the recollection of facts or events in the immediate past.

reciprocal inhibition and desensitization: A term for a widely used form of behavior therapy. The patient is made comfortable in relaxed, pleasant, supportive surroundings and is then exposed, usually by imagery, to gradually increasing amounts of anxiety-provoking stimuli. The feeling of comfort associated with the situation allows the patient to tolerate increasing amounts of these stimuli and may eventually entirely remove their ability to arouse anxiety.

reference, delusion of (idea of): See *ideas of reference.*

regression: The partial or symbolic return to more infantile patterns of reacting. Manifested in a wide variety of circumstances such as normal sleep, play, severe physical illness, and in many psychiatric disorders.

rehabilitation: The methods and techniques used in a program that seeks to achieve maximal functional and optimal adjustment for the identified patient, and to prevent relapses or recurrences of his condition (because of the latter, sometimes termed *tertiary prevention*). The focus in rehabilitation is on the patient's assets and recoverable functions, rather than on the liabilities engendered by his pathology or the complications of disuse and social deterioration which formerly were often mistakenly considered to be part of the underlying disease process. Includes individual and group psychotherapy, directed socialization, vocational retraining, education. See *community psychiatry*.

REM sleep: One of two kinds of sleep. The term designates the "deep sleep" periods during which the sleeper makes coordinated rapid eye movements (REM's) resembling purposeful fixation shifts, as might be seen in the waking state. REM sleep is also called "dreaming sleep" since there appears to be an intimate relationship with dreaming activity, as if the dreamer were watching the visual imagery of his dream. *NREM* sleep is the term given to the longer period of sleep that begins as the subject passes from wakefulness into a light sleep with *no rapid eye movements* (NREM's). REM sleep interrupts NREM sleep about once in every ninety minutes and lasts for about twenty minutes. REM sleep is believed to account for one-fifth to one-fourth of the total sleep time. Between the two forms of sleep, there are distinct differences in the *EEG* patterns and in the occulomotor, cardiovascular, respiratory, muscular, and other bodily activities.

remission: Abatement of an illness.

remotivation: A group treatment technique administered by nursing service personnel in a mental hospital; of particular value to long-term, withdrawn patients by way of stimulating their communication skills and interest in their environment.

repetition compulsion: In psychoanalytic theory the impulse to reenact earlier emotional experiences. Considered by Freud more fundamental than the *pleasure principle*. According to Ernest Jones: "The blind impulse to repeat earlier experiences and situations quite irrespective of any advantage that doing so might bring from a pleasure-pain point of view."

repress: A *defense mechanism,* operating unconsciously, that banishes unacceptable ideas, affects, or impulses, from consciousness or that keeps out of consciousness what has never been conscious. Although not subject to voluntary recall, the repressed material may emerge in disguised form. Sometimes used as a generic term for all *defense mechanisms.* Often confused with the conscious mechanism of *suppression.*

resident: An M.D. who has completed his internship and who is in graduate training to qualify as a specialist in a particular field of medicine, such as psychiatry. The *American Board of Psychiatry and Neurology* requires three years of psychiatric residency training in an approved hospital or clinic, together with two years of practice in the specialty of psychiatry, to qualify for examinations.

resistance: In psychiatry, the individual's conscious or unconscious psychological defense against bringing repressed (unconscious) thoughts to light. See also *mental mechanism.*

retardation: Slowing down of mental and physical activity. Most frequently seen in severe depressions, which are sometimes spoken of as retarded depressions. Also a synonym for *mental retardation.*

retrograde amnesia: See *amnesia.*

retrospective falsification: Unconscious distortion of past experiences to conform to present emotional needs.

rigidity: In psychiatry, refers to an individual's excessive resistance to change.

ritual: In psychiatry, any psychomotor activity sustained by an individual to relieve anxiety. Most commonly seen in *obsessive compulsive neurosis* (q.v. under *neurosis*).

RNA: Abbreviation for *ribonucleic acid.* A vital nucleic acid manufactured by *DNA.* Essential for the building of body proteins from amino acids. Appears to play a key role in memory.

Rorschach test: A *projective test* developed by the Swiss psychiatrist, Hermann Rorschach (1844-1922), which seeks to disclose conscious and unconscious personality traits and emotional conflicts through eliciting the patient's associations to a standard set of ink-blots.

Rush, Benjamin (1745-1813): Early American physician, signer of the Declaration of Independence, and author of the first American text on psychiatry (1812). He is called "the father of American psychiatry."

---

sadism: See *sexual deviation.*

satyriasis: Pathologic or exaggerated sexual drive or excitement in the male. May be of psychic or organic etiology. Analogous to *nymphomania* in the female.

schizoid personality: See under *personality disorders.*

schizophrenia: A large group of disorders, usually of psychotic proportion, manifested by characteristic disturbances of thought, mood, and behavior. Thought disturbances are marked by alterations of concept formation that may lead to misinterpretation of reality and sometimes to *delusions* and *hallucinations.* Mood changes include ambivalence, constriction, inappropriateness, and loss of empathy with others. Behavior may be withdrawn, regressive, and bizarre. Currently recognized types of schizophrenia are:

> **acute schizophrenic episode:** A condition characterized by the acute onset of schizophrenic symptoms, often associated with confusion, perplexity, *ideas of reference,* emotional turmoil, excitement, depression, fear, or dream-like dissociation. This term is *not* applicable to acute episodes of the other types of schizophrenia described here.

catatonic type: A schizophrenic disorder manifested in either or both of two ways: (1) by excessive and sometimes violent motor activity and excitement ("excited subtype") or (2) by generalized inhibition manifested as *stupor, mutism, negativism,* or *waxy flexibility* ("withdrawn subtype").

childhood schizophrenia: Schizophrenia appearing before puberty. It is frequently manifested by *autism* and withdrawn behavior; failure to develop an identity separate from the mother's; and general unevenness, gross immaturity, and inadequacy in development.

chronic undifferentiated type: A condition manifested by definite signs of schizophrenic thought, affect, and behavior that are of a sufficiently mixed or indefinite type that they defy classification into one of the other types of schizophrenia.

hebephrenic type: A schizophrenic disorder characterized by disorganized thinking, shallow and inappropriate affect, inappropriate giggling, silly and regressive behavior and mannerisms, and frequent hypochondriacal complaints. Delusions and hallucinations are usually bizarre and not well organized.

latent type: A condition manifested by clear symptoms of schizophrenia but no history of psychotic schizophrenic episodes. Sometimes designated as incipient, pre-psychotic, pseudo-neurotic, pseudo-psychopathic, or borderline schizophrenia.

paranoid type: A schizophrenic disorder characterized primarily by the presence of persecutory or grandiose delusions, often associated with hallucinations.

process schizophrenia: Unofficial term for schizophrenia attributed more to organic factors than to environmental ones; typically begins gradually, continues chronically, and progresses (either rapidly or slowly) to an irreversible psychosis. See also *reactive schizophrenia,* to which this condition is contrasted.

reactive schizophrenia: Unofficial term for schizophrenia attributed primarily to strong predisposing and/or precipitating environmental factors; usually of rapid onset and brief duration, with the affected individual appearing well both before and after the schizophrenic episode. Differentiating this condition from *process schizophrenia* is generally considered more important in Europe than in this country.

residual type: A condition manifested by individuals with signs of schizophrenia who, following a psychotic schizophrenic episode, are no longer psychotic.

school phobia: A term used when a child, usually a pupil in the early elementary grades, unexpectedly and without apparent reason, strenuously refuses to attend school because of some irrational fear. The underlying psychopathology is believed to be an intense *separation anxiety* rooted in unresolved dependency ties.

scotoma: In psychiatry, a figurative blind spot in an individual's psychologic awareness.

screen memory: A consciously tolerable memory that serves as a cover or "screen" for another associated memory that would be disturbing and emotionally painful if recalled.

secondary gain: The external gain that is derived from any illness such as personal attention and service, monetary gains, disability benefits, and release from unpleasant responsibility. See also *primary gain.*

secondary process: In psychoanalytic theory, mental activity and thinking characteristic of the *ego* and influenced by the demands of the environment. Characterized by organization, systematization, intellectualization, and similar processes leading to logical thought and action in adult life. See also *primary process.*

sedative: A broad term applied to any agent that quiets or calms or allays excitement. While *narcotics, hypnotics* and other classes of drugs have calming properties, the term is generally restricted to drugs that are not primarily used to achieve analgesia or sleep. See also *psychopharmacology.*

senile dementia: A chronic *organic brain syndrome* associated with generalized atrophy of the brain due to aging. In addition to the organic symptoms present, self-centeredness, difficulty assimilating new experiences, and childish emotionality are usually prominent. Deterioration may range from minimal to severe.

sensorium: Roughly synonymous with consciousness. Includes the special sensory perceptive powers and their central correlation and integration in the brain. A clear sensorium conveys the presence of a reasonably accurate memory together with a correct orientation for time, place, and person.

sensory aphasia: See *speech disturbance.*

sensory deprivation: Term for experience of being cut off from usual external stimuli and the opportunity for perception. May occur experimentally or accidentally in various ways such as through loss of hearing or eyesight, by becoming marooned, by solitary confinement, by assignment to a remote service post, or by travelling in space. May lead to disorganized thinking, *depression, panic, delusions,* and *hallucinations.*

separation anxiety: The fear and apprehension noted in infants when removed from their mothers (or surrogates) or when approached by strangers. Most marked from sixth to tenth month. In later life, similar reaction may be caused by separation from significant persons or familiar surroundings.

serotonin: A *biogenic amine* derived from tryptophan. Present in the intestine and the brain. A smooth muscle constrictor or stimulator. May influence nervous system activity. See also *indoles.*

sexual deviation: The direction of sexual interest toward objects other than persons of the opposite sex, toward sexual acts not associated with coitus, or toward coitus performed under bizarre circumstances. Examples are:

bestiality: Sexual relations between human and animal.

exhibitionism: Psychiatrically, body exposure, usually of the male genitals to females.

fetishism: A sexual deviation characterized by attachment of special meaning to an inanimate object (or *fetish*) which serves, usually unconsciously, as a substitute for the original object or person. The fetish is essential for completion of orgasm. Rare in females.

homosexuality: Sexual attraction or relationship between members of the same sex. **Overt homosexuality:** Homosexuality that is consciously recognized or practiced. **Latent homosexuality:** A condition characterized by unconscious homosexual desires. See also *lesbian*.

masochism: Pleasure derived from physical or psychological pain inflicted either by onself or by others. When it is consciously sought as a part of the sexual act or as a prerequisite to sexual gratification, it is classifiable as a sexual deviation. It is the converse of *sadism,* and the two tend to coexist in the same individual.

pederasty: Homosexual intercourse between man and boy by anus.

pedophilia: In psychiatry, a sexual deviation involving the use of children for sexual purposes.

sadism: Pleasure derived from inflicting physical or psychological pain or abuse on others. The sexual significance of sadistic wishes or behavior may be conscious or unconscious. When necessary for sexual gratification, classifiable as a sexual deviation.

sodomy: Anal intercourse. Legally, the term may include other types of perversion such as *bestiality*.

transvestitism (transvestism): Sexual pleasure derived from dressing or masquerading in the clothing of the opposite sex. The sexual origins of transvestitism may be unconscious. There is a strong wish to appear as and to be accepted as a member of the opposite sex.

voyeurism: Sexually-motivated and often compulsive interest in watching or looking at others, particularly at genitals. Roughly synonymous with "peeping Tom." Found predominantly in males.

shell-shock: Obsolete term used in World War I to designate a wide variety of psychotic and neurotic disorders presumably due to combat experience. See *conversion, combat fatigue, hysterical neurosis*.

shock treatment: A form of psychiatric treatment in which electric current, insulin, carbon dioxide, or Indoklon®, is administered to the patient and results in a loss of consciousness or a convulsive or comatose reaction to alter favorably the course of the illness. Some common types of shock therapy are:

carbon dioxide therapy: A form of inhalation treatment in which carbon dioxide gas is administered to the point of unconsciousness in order to cause emotional *abreactions* and alleviation of anxiety.

electroconvulsive treatment (ECT): Use of electric current to induce unconsciousness and/or convulsive seizures. Most effective in the treatment of depression. Introduced by Cerletti and Bini in 1938. Modifications are electronarcosis, producing sleep-like states, and electrostimulation, which avoids convulsions.

Indoklon therapy: A form of shock treatment in which a convulsive seizure is produced by intravenous injection or inhalation of the drug, Indoklon.

insulin coma therapy (ICT): A treatment primarily for schizophrenia in which insulin is injected in large enough doses to produce profound hypoglycemia (low blood sugar) resulting in coma. First used by Manfred Sakel in 1933. Its use in the United States has decreased since the introduction of *tranquilizers.*

Metrazol shock therapy: A form of shock treatment, now rarely used, in which a convulsive seizure is produced by intravenous injection of Metrazol (known as Cardiazol in Europe). Introduced by L. von Meduna in 1935.

subcoma insulin treatment: A treatment in which insulin is administered to induce drowsiness or somnolence short of coma. Used to alleviate anxiety, stimulate appetite, and induce a feeling of well being.

sibling: Term for a full brother or sister.

sibling rivalry: The competition between *siblings* for the love of a parent or for other recognition or gain.

situational depression: See *depressive neurosis* under *neurosis.*

social control: The way in which society or any of its subgroups, various institutions, organizations, and agencies exert influence upon the individual, or groups of individuals, to conform to the expectations and requirements of that society or subgroup. Control may be coercive (as by means of the law) or persuasive (through such devices as suggestion, blame, praise, reward, and recognition). See also *sociology*.

social psychiatry: The field of psychiatry concerned with the cultural, ecologic, and sociologic factors that engender, precipitate, intensify, prolong, or otherwise complicate maladaptive patterns of behavior and their treatment; sometimes used synonymously with *community psychiatry,* although some limit the latter term to practical or clinical applications of social psychiatry. Important in social psychiatry is the ecological approach to maladaptive behavior, which is viewed not only as a deviation of an individual but also as a reflection of deviation in the social systems in which he lives.

social work: The use of community resources and of the conscious adaptive capacities of individuals and groups to better the adjustment of an individual to his environment and to improve the quality and functioning of an individual's external environment.

social worker, psychiatric: A social worker with specialized psychiatric training leading to a graduate degree (M.S.W. or D.S.W.) in social work. Such a worker may utilize all social work techniques such as case work, group work, and community organization in a psychiatric or mental health setting.

socialization: The process by which society integrates the individual and the way in which the individual learns to become a functioning member of that society. See *sociology*.

sociology: The study of the development and governing principles of social organization and the group behavior of men, in contrast to the individual behavior of man. Overlaps to some extent with *cultural anthropology*. Related concepts are defined elsewhere under the following terms: *alienation, social control, socialization*.

sociopath: An unofficial term for *antisocial personality* (q.v. under *personality disorders*).

sodomy: See *sexual deviation*.

soma: The body.

somatic conversion: See under *neurosis, hysterical.*

somatization reactions: See *psychophysiologic disorders.*

somnambulism: Sleepwalking. A dissociated or a fugue-like state in which the person can move about but otherwise is asleep.

speech disturbance: Any disorder of verbal or nonverbal communication that is not due to faulty innervation of the speech muscles or organs of articulation. There is no single cause for any of the speech disturbances, but minimal cortical or subcortical dysfunction, including dysharmony in the physiologic predominance of one cerebral hemisphere over the other, may be an important factor in many patients. Any grouping is highly arbitrary, but the term includes many language and *learning disturbances,* such as those listed below:

> **aphasia:** Inability to utter a sound, word, or phrase, or to find the right name for an object. **Sensory aphasia:** Inability to perceive or understand certain sounds, syllables, or phrases, as in word-blindness. **Central** or **syntactical aphasia:** Speech is fluent but disordered by verbal and grammatical confusions (paraphasia).

> **alexia (dyslexia):** Inability or difficulty in reading, including word-blindness and strephosymbolia (tendency to reverse letters and words in reading and writing).

> **agraphia (dysgraphia):** Inability or disability in writing.

> **amimia:** Inability to gesticulate or to understand the significance of gestures.

> **apraxia:** Loss of previously acquired skilled acts (including speech and writing) or failure to develop normal skills.

Stanford-Binet intelligence scale: An individually administered intelligence test emphasizing verbal facility. Used with individuals from age two through adulthood. The test yields a *mental age* and an *IQ.*

status epilepticus: More or less continuous epileptic seizures. See *epilepsy.*

stereotypy: Persistent mechanical repetition of speech or motor activity. Observed, for example, in *schizophrenia.*

strephosymbolia: See *speech disturbance.*

stress reaction: See *gross stress reaction.*

stroke: Apoplexy; cerebrovascular accident (CVA); gross cerebral hemorrhage or softening of the brain following hemorrhage, thrombosis, or embolism of the cerebral arteries. Symptoms may include coma, paralysis (particularly on one side of the body), convulsions, aphasia, and other neurologic symptoms determined by the location of the lesion.

stupor: In psychiatry, a state in which the individual does not react to his surroundings and appears to be unaware of them. In catatonic stupor, the unawareness is more apparent than real. See *catatonic state.*

stuttering and stammering: Spasmodic speaking with involuntary halts and repetitions, usually considered of psychogenic origin.

subcoma insulin treatment: See under *shock treatment.*

subconscious: Obsolescent term in psychiatry. Formerly used to include the *preconscious* (what can be recalled with effort) and the *unconscious.*

subcoma insulin treatment: See *shock therapy.*

sublimation: A *defense mechanism,* operating unconsciously, by which instinctual drives, consciously unacceptable, are diverted into personally and socially acceptable channels.

substitution: A *defense mechanism,* operating unconsciously, by which an unattainable or unacceptable goal, emotion, or object is replaced by one that is more attainable or acceptable. Comparable to *displacement.*

succinylcholine: A potent chemical used intravenously in anesthesia as a skeletal muscle relaxant. Also used prior to electroconvulsive therapy to minimize the possibility of fractures.

suggestion: In psychiatry, the process of influencing an individual to accept uncritically an idea, belief, or attitude induced by the therapist.

Sullivan, Harry Stack (1892-1949): American psychiatrist best known for his interpersonal theory of psychiatry, in which human behavior and personality development are described in terms of the sum total of the interpersonal relations of the individual.

superego: In psychoanalytic theory, that part of the personality associated with ethics, standards, and self-criticism. It is formed by the infant's identification with important and esteemed persons in his early life, particularly parents. The supposed or actual wishes of these significant persons are taken over as part of the child's own personal standards to help form the "conscience." In late life they may become anachronistic and self-punitive, especially in neurotic persons. See also *ego, id.*

supportive psychotherapy: A technique of psychotherapy that aims to reinforce a patient's defense and to help him suppress disturbing psychological material. Supportive psychotherapy utilizes such measures as inspiration, reassurance, suggestion, persuasion, counselling, and re-education. It avoids probing the patient's emotional conflicts in depth.

suppression: The conscious effort to control and conceal unacceptable impulses, thoughts, feelings, or acts.

surrogate: One who takes the place of another; a substitute person. In psychiatry, usually refers to an authority figure who replaces a parent in the emotional feelings of the patient (e.g. father-surrogate, mother-surrogate).

symbiosis: In psychiatry, denotes a mutually-reinforcing relationship between two disturbed persons who are dependent on each other.

symbolization: An unconscious mental process operating by *association* and based on similarity and abstract representation whereby one object or idea comes to stand for another through some part, quality, or aspect which the two have in common. The symbol carries in more or less disguised form the emotional feelings vested in the initial object or idea.

sympathetic nervous system: That part of the *autonomic nervous system* that responds to dangerous or threatening situations by preparing the individual physiologically for "fight or flight." See also *parasympathetic nervous system.*

sympathy: Compassion for another's grief or loss. To be differentiated from *empathy*.

symptom: A specific manifestation of a patient's condition indicative of an abnormal physical or mental state. Psychiatric symptoms are often the result of unconscious conflict and may represent in symbolic form an instinctual wish, the defense against such a wish, or a compromise between the two.

syndrome: A configuration of symptoms that occur together and that constitute a recognizable condition. Example: *Ganser's syndrome.*

syntactical (central) aphasia: See *speech disturbance.*

syphilis: A venereal disease, which, if untreated, may lead to *central nervous system* deterioration with psychotic manifestations in its later stages. See *general paralysis.*

t-groups (sensitivity training groups): A group of people who meet to learn about themselves, about interpersonal relationships, about *group process,* and about larger social systems. An important element in the learning is that the group members meet in an unstructured situation and have the task of constructing their own group.

Talion law or principle: A primitive, unrealistic belief, usually unconsicous, conforming to the Biblical injunction of an "eye for an eye" and a "tooth for a tooth." In psychoanalysis, the concept and fear that all injury, actual or intended, will be punished in kind—i.e. retaliated.

telepathy: The communication of thought from one person to another without the intervention of physical means. Not generally accepted as scientifically valid. See also *extrasensory perception*.

thematic apperception test (TAT): A *projective test* consisting of a series of drawings suggesting life situations, which may be variously interpreted depending on the mood and personality of the subject.

therapeutic community: A term of British origin, now widely used, for a specially structured mental hospital milieu that encourages patients to function within the range of social norms. Special educational techniques are used to overcome the patients' dependency needs, to encourage them to assume personal responsibility, and to speed their social rehabilitation.

tic: An intermittent, involuntary, spasmodic movement such as a muscular twitch, often without a demonstrable external stimulus. A tic may be a disguised expression of a hidden emotional conflict or the result of neurologic disease.

toilet training: The methods used by a child's parents, usually the mother, in teaching and encouraging control of bladder and bowel functions. Occurs at an important period in the formation of the child's personality. Marks the parents' first major effort to control the child and the child's first good chance to resist the parents. Adult attitudes about cleanliness, control, authority, and anger arise in part from this period of toilet training and the method by which it is carried out.

topectomy: A type of *psychosurgery*.

total push therapy: In a hospital setting, the energetic simultaneous application of all available psychiatric therapies to the treatment of a patient, first described by Abraham Myerson (1881-1948). Myerson emphasized physical activity, recreation, praise, blame, reward, punishment, and involvement in care of clothing and personal hygiene.

toxic psychosis: A *psychosis* resulting from the toxic effect of chemicals and drugs, including those produced in the body.

trance: A state of diminished activity and consciousness resembling sleep. Seen in hypnosis, hysteria, and ecstatic religious states.

tranquilizer: A drug that decreases anxiety and agitation, usually without causing drowsiness. Divided into two groups:

major tranquilizers: Drugs such as *phenothiazines* which produce relief from symptoms of psychosis.

minor tranquilizers: Drugs that are used predominantly to diminish neurotic anxiety.

transactional analysis: A psychodynamic approach that attempts to understand the interplay between therapist and patient — and ultimately between the patient and external reality — in terms of role theory, beginning with an exposure of current, well-defined, explicit roles, and ultimately evoking a recognition of implicit emotional roles and a repetition of earlier interactions that trace the genesis of current behavior.

transcultural psychiatry: See *cultural psychiatry.*

transference: The unconscious "transfer" to others of feelings and attitudes that were originally associated with important figures (parents, siblings, etc.) in one's early life. The transference relationship follows roughly the pattern of its prototype. The psychiatrist utilizes this phenomenon as a therapeutic tool to help the patient understand his emotional problems and their origin. In the patient-physician relationship the transference may be negative (hostile) or positive (affectionate). See also *countertransference.*

transient situational disturbance: A more or less transient disorder of any severity (including psychosis) that represents an acute reaction to overwhelming stress, such as the severe crying spells, loss of appetite, and social withdrawal of a child separated from its mother; or, in an adult, a reaction to an unwanted pregnancy manifested by suicidal gestures and hostile complaints. The symptoms generally recede as the stress diminishes.

transorbital lobotomy: A type of *psychosurgery.*

transsexualism: A term used to describe the wish to change one's sex. Often associated with *transvestitism* and *homosexuality,* it may be manifested by seeking plastic surgery to replace the male's external genitalia with an artificial vagina, electrolysis to remove facial hair, estrogens to stimulate breast enlargement, etc. Also known as "sex-role inversion," transsexualism is believed to have its pathological origins in early childhood, when the future transsexual develops a primary and continuing identification with the parent of the opposite sex and adopts the *gender role* of that parent. See also *gender identity*.

transvestitism (transvestism): See *sexual deviation*.

trauma: In psychiatry, an extremely upsetting emotional experience that may aggravate or contribute to a mental disorder. In medicine, any injury or wound.

traumatic neurosis: The term encompasses combat, occupational, and compensation neuroses. These are neurotic reactions that have been attributed to or follow a situational traumatic event, or series of events. Usually the event has some specific and symbolic emotional significance for the patient. The neurosis may be reinforced by *secondary gain*.

triage. The sorting out and classification of casualties. An essential function for carrying out efficient treatment in war, civil disasters, and other situations where limited resources must be organized to provide service for large numbers of people.

trisomy: The presence of three *chromosomes* instead of the two that normally represent each potential set of chromosomes. Humans have 23 sets of chromosomes. The most significant trisomy in psychiatry is that associated with *Down's syndrome*.

Tuke, William 1732-1822): English Quaker layman who pioneered in the treatment of patients without physical restraints.

unconditioned reflex (UCR): An inborn physiologic reflex response to a stimulus; e.g. salivation at the sight of food.

unconscious: In Freudian theory, that part of the mind or mental functioning of which the content is only rarely subject to awareness. It is a repository for data that have never been conscious (primary repression), or that may have become conscious briefly and later repressed (secondary repression).

underachiever: Term used in psychiatry for a person who manifestly does not function up to his capacity.

undoing: A primitive *defense mechanism,* operating unconsciously, in which something unacceptable and already done is symbolically acted out in reverse, usually repetitiously, in the hope of "undoing" it and thus relieving anxiety.

vaginismus: Painful vaginal spasm, usually occurring in connection with sexual intercourse.

vegetative nervous system: Obsolescent term for the *autonomic nervous system.*

verbigeration: Stereotyped and seemingly meaningless repetition of words or sentences.

vertigo: A type of dizziness or "spinning around," in which the subject feels that he or his environment is spinning. Often associated with faintness.

vitamin therapy: See *pellagra.*

voluntary admission: See under *commitment.*

voyeurism: See *sexual deviation.*

WAIS (Wechsler Adult Intelligence Scale): A verbal and performance test especially designed to measure intelligence in adults.

waxy flexibility: See *cerea flexibilitas.*

weekend hospital: See under *partial hospitalization.*

Weyer, Johann (circa 1530): Dutch physician who was one of the first to devote his major interest to psychiatric disorders. Regarded by some as the founder of modern psychiatry.

White, William Alanson (1870-1937): American psychiatrist famous for his early support of psychoanalysis and his contributions to forensic psychiatry.

withdrawal: In psychiatry, a pathological retreat from people or the world of reality, often seen in *schizophrenia.*

withdrawal symptoms: Term used to describe physical and

mental effects of withdrawing drugs from patients who have become habituated or addicted to them. The physical symptoms may include nausea, vomiting, tremors, abdominal pain, and convulsions.

word-blindness: See *speech disturbance.*

word salad: A mixture of words and phrases that lack comprehensive meaning or logical coherence, commonly seen in schizophrenic states.

working through: Active exploration of a problem by patient and therapist until a satisfactory solution has been found or until a symptom has been traced to its unconscious sources.

xenophobia: See under *phobia.*